SUPER AGING

SUPER AGING

Outsmart the Effects of
Conventional Aging and Live
Like You are Decades Younger

JEFF CORY

To my mom and dad who shared with me and modeled a life-changing gift—the delight and blessings that come from treasuring our elders.

Preface

For nearly three decades, I've coached, mentored, and advised hundreds of retirees as the founding Executive Director of the Legacy Foundation at Shell Point. For more than 50 years, Shell Point—one of America's largest nationally recognized, award-winning, continuing care retirement communities—has set the standard for retirement living with unparalleled lifestyle and comprehensive care.

But the most remarkable thing about Shell Point is its residents. They live nearly 10 years longer than the average American. I call them *Super Agers.*

What are the keys to a long and healthy life?

How can we age better today than our parents and grandparents did?

Can we minimize the effects of aging and make living to age 100 or beyond commonplace?

How can we make our later years better and more fulfilling?

We all hope for some amazing discovery that will guarantee us a longer, healthier life. But here's the good news—you don't have to wait for miraculous breakthroughs. You can live a long, healthy, vibrant life now.

You can reframe aging and take an active role in your overall health and well-being. You can outsmart the effects of conventional aging and live like you were decades younger.

Welcome to Super Aging!

This holistic approach could increase your life expectancy and improve your quality of life. Super Aging is living by a biological calendar instead of a chronological timeline. Age 70 could look and feel like 60 or even 50. You could still be active and productive at 80, 95, or maybe 100.

And all this is mostly your choice as you establish a Super Aging lifestyle and mindset that break down the barriers that have made you age far too soon.

You've picked up this book and started reading it, so I know you're ready to discover how to live a fuller, healthier life that defies your age. Get ready for a journey that will give you a fresh outlook on your lifestyle, your determination, your health, and your age.

Join me on this life-changing journey as I share with you what I have learned from one of the world's most spectacular Super Aging communities. I truly believe this book will profoundly impact your life and help transform you into a Super Ager!

Jeff Cory
"Champion for Super Aging"

Table of Contents

The Super Aging Framework

Change the way you look at things,
and the things you look at change.

—Wayne Dyer

Imagine that someone hands you a gift—a gift that at first seems ordinary and unassuming. As you untie the ribbon and peel back the paper, amazing things begin to unfold. You realize it is a gift with the potential to revitalize your life. This unassuming package holds the key to an incredible, meaningful, extraordinary future—more than you could ever hope for or imagine. The gift is called Super Aging, and it's yours for the taking.

Super Agers have discovered the secrets of outsmarting the effects of aging and are living as though they were decades younger. With a mind, body, and soul approach, Super Agers are breaking conventional stereotypes and forging a new and better path for health, happiness, and longevity.

America's obsession with youthfulness has stifled aging adults far too long. The fear of aging, also known as *gerascophobia*, has encouraged negative stereotypes and irrational behaviors that are causing people to hold on to youth at all costs. The word *gerascophobia* is derived from the Greek *tha geraso* ("I am getting old") and *phobos* ("dread or deep fear").

This fear includes looking older, deteriorating physically and mentally, ending up lonely and isolated, and eventually becoming obsolete in society. These conventional ways of thinking about aging are causing people to live the last 30+ years of their lives feeling old and incapable.

This pattern of thinking has ballooned into scores of unhealthy Americans who are experiencing a myriad of chronic diseases—cancer, diabetes, arthritis, heart disease, mental illness, cognitive decline—that are often preventable. Even more disturbing is that the United States just ranked 46th in the world for life expectancy.[1]

While diseases and aging issues are valid concerns, they aren't absolutes, and they certainly don't have to define seniors. The bottom line is that America needs an attitude adjustment. As we become an aging society with people living longer than ever before, the writing is on the wall—conventional aging isn't cutting it.

Here is what conventional agers mistakenly believe:

- Their valuable contributions to society are over.
- They are meant to be alone without meaningful relationships or connections.
- Their physical and mental declines are inevitable aspects of aging.
- They will retire and live the rest of their lives in boredom.
- They are stuck in their ways and unable to change.
- They view their age as a limit, letting it steal their enjoyment, purpose, and meaning in life.

In contrast, here's what Super Agers believe:

- They have much to offer the world, the workplace, and society.
- Their family, friends, and connections are essential to a full life.
- They must keep their minds healthy and sharp through determination, utilization, and a positive outlook.
- They want to live, love, grow, and experience life to its fullest.
- Their days include new opportunities to live with creativity, curiosity, and purpose.
- Their age is only a number, and it's their life choices, attitudes, and habits that determine their biological age.

Do you see the difference? Do you see how conventional beliefs about aging are destructive and detrimental to longevity?

To drive it home further, conventional agers use words like *old*, *worn out*, *frail*, *used up*, *no good*, *incapable*, and more. Super Agers, on the other hand, speak affirming words such as *wise, mature, strong, healthy, worthy, more than capable*, and so on. The contrast is clear— conventional agers limit themselves by holding onto false attitudes and beliefs, while Super Agers free themselves from limits and create a lifestyle that is healthy, whole, and complete.

Satchel Paige, National Baseball Hall of Fame pitcher and oldest player in baseball history, once said, "How old would you be if you didn't know how old you are?" Those are profound words! Paige didn't let age—or any other stereotype—stop him from making his debut into Major League Baseball at the age of 42 after a stellar career in the Negro League. As the first Black pitcher to play in the American League, he was all about pushing past conventional boundaries. Even with his late start in the majors, he was known for pitching nothing but fastballs— most that were unhittable—for the better part of 15 years. According to sportswriter Joe Posnanski, Paige was "perhaps the most precise pitcher in baseball history."[2] It was this kind of Super Ager tenacity that eventually led this ageless wonder to pitch three scoreless innings for the Kansas City Athletics on September 25, 1965, at the age of 59.

Super Agers put no limits on their age or quality of life. Instead, they follow in the footsteps of these renowned Super Agers:

- Nelson Mandela – became president of South Africa at the age of 76
- Judi Dench –an Oscar-winning British actress who is still going strong at 86
- Grandma Moses – created 1,600 paintings after the age of 75
- J. R. R. Tolkien – wrote *The Lord of the Rings* at age 62
- James Parkinson – discovered Parkinson's disease at the age of 62

These Super Agers and countless more have discarded old beliefs about age and embraced the Super Aging lifestyle. Through step-by-step planning and executing, seniors are finding amazing success by implementing their framework and key pillars for longevity. Let's look at the framework and pillars we'll be covering in this book.

Mindset: Moving from Fear to Empowerment

When you change your mindset, the fear of aging is replaced with confidence and empowerment. You'll examine your thought patterns, attitudes, and beliefs about aging as you develop a Super Aging mindset. In time, your fears will be turned into plans of action with a sense of purpose and empowerment.

Health & Wellness Lifestyle: Achieving Better Health for a Better You

You'll see *exactly* how to develop a promising plan of action and implement habits that will transform your life and your perspective on health. The Super Aging Health & Wellness Quiz will give you a clear starting point, and the incremental lifestyle changes that follow will quickly become your new way of living.

Relationships: Staying Connected during Retirement

Relationships are one of the most important driving factors of happiness, so we should take them very seriously. You'll see how happiness in marriage is linked to longevity and how a few deep friendships are more important than many superficial ones. You'll discover how to balance your relationship with your children and extended family members. Connection is at the heart of the Super Aging lifestyle.

Retirement Readiness: Preparing Your Finances for Retirement

Of all your worries about aging, financial security is probably at the top of your list. The financial framework in this book will ease your fears and help you create a solid, workable plan—no matter what your financial situation is. It will address every aspect of your financial future, including budgeting, saving, investing, and long-term care to show you exactly how to prepare for your future.

Purpose: Discovering Your Destiny

Super Agers have a heightened desire to reinvent themselves—to take their unique strengths and use them for a higher purpose. You'll discover your unique gifts and reimagine your destiny. You'll see the importance of your influence on those closest to you and on the world. You'll see clearly the path of a compassion-driven life and legacy.

Emotional Mastery: Avoiding the 7 Deadly Sins of Aging

The Super Aging approach to managing and mastering your emotions will revitalize your life. Not only will you learn how to overcome fear, negativity, loneliness, depression, and loss, but you'll discover the importance of brain health and how you can actually improve your emotional intelligence to avoid the 7 deadly sins of aging.

Home & Community: Discovering the Best Place to Super Age

The framework for home and community will help you focus on what matters most and discover the keys to finding a great place to Super Age. You'll look at everything from aging in place to relocating to your dream destination. With a major focus on your quality of life, the home and community aspect will transform the way you view retirement.

Perks: Amazing Things No One Told You about Aging

You'll begin to see Super Aging as a sort of Renaissance, a time of rebirth, revival, and creativity. Your retirement years will become not about survival but about revival. You'll take center stage as the curtain opens to the perks of Super Aging and things no one ever told you about aging. You'll see life as new opportunities for personal growth and transformation.

In America: How Super Agers Respond to Growing Trends

What trends are impacting Super Agers today? How should you respond to those trends? It's a common saying that older people don't like change, but what if changing statistics, new developments, and innovative technology have a positive impact on your life and give you more freedom? We'll look at all the growing trends in our world today and see how you can benefit from them.

Champion: Taking the Next Step

In the final chapter, you'll see the importance of making a plan and pinpointing your future. You'll visualize your journey as a Super Ager and take the 90-day challenge to improve your life and gain momentum. You'll see the tangible results of developing new health habits, being intentional, and cultivating relationships that truly matter.

The Reward

As you begin to gain traction with each of these pillars, you'll eventually generate unstoppable momentum. Through something called the *multiplier effect*, each small, consistent step will precipitate great change. And change is what we're after!

The reward of embracing *your* Super Aging lifestyle will be the reward of ultimate *freedom*. In the rawest sense of the word, you'll be free to live, think, prosper, and thrive without the limits of stereotypical, conventional aging. Throwing off every restraint common to older adults in America, you'll be free to pursue your best life *now* and for many years to come.

So what does successful aging look like to you? What stereotypes about aging do you need to personally overcome? What challenges and opportunities can you identify in order to become a Super Ager?

In this book you'll find solid answers to these and many other questions. You'll be inspired to leave conventional beliefs about aging behind. And ultimately, you'll be empowered to reframe your aging journey and forge a new path of confident, healthy, intentional living. So keep reading, keep discovering, and keep believing. Your Super Aging lifestyle is about to begin.

The Super Aging Mindset:
Moving from Fear to Empowerment

The extent to which our lives are full and rich is up to us.
Age is not the barrier; mindset is.

—LeAura Alderson

Uh-oh. That's often the first thought of someone who wakes up one day and comes face to face with the fact that they are aging. It's during that pivotal moment that some people spring into fight-or-flight mode and do everything in their power to stop it. Others throw their hands up in defeat. There are still others who determine to live differently. They develop a Super Aging mindset that supersedes the traditional way of thinking about age and invites a sense of opportunity, adventure, and empowerment.

What kind of "ager" are you?

- Are you consumed with worry about the future?
- Are you constantly trying to stop the aging process through whatever means necessary?
- Have you given in to old age thinking and believe you have nothing left to offer?

Wherever you are in the aging process, it's not too late to change your mindset—and thus the course of your life. As we learned in Chapter One, Super Aging defines people who are *mentally or physically capable of performing as if they were decades younger.* While a small percentage of people naturally fit into this category, others choose to embrace it as a way of confidently navigating their retirement years.

In this chapter, we'll explore what it means to have a Super Aging mindset that will help you clearly define a solid framework for the rest of your life. You will evaluate some long-held attitudes, cast aside widely held aging stereotypes, and change a few habits. This chapter will challenge your way of thinking and how you process information. It will encourage you to build new thought paths that build confidence to take you where you want to go.

According to Harvard Health Publishing, "Super-agers keep moving out of their comfort zones to gain new areas of expertise."[1] With this Super Aging mindset, you'll be challenged to think outside the box, explore new concepts, and ultimately gain the confidence you need to outsmart aging.

So, are you ready? Let's look at a few mindsets that are key to the Super Aging lifestyle.

A New Beginning

The first step in developing a Super Aging mindset is to view wherever you are, no matter your age, as the beginning instead of the end. It's the start of a new era, a time to embrace change and launch a new lifestyle. Look at it as the beginning of the rest of your life!

In his book, *Retire Inspired*, author and financial adviser Chris Hogan says this: "One of the first steps to take on the road to your dream retirement is to realize we're not just talking about the end of your life. When some people hear the word *retirement*, they immediately start thinking of death."[2]

Retirement does not equal death. It equals opportunity. For the first time in your life, you have the opportunity to:

- create your own schedule.
- explore new hobbies and passions.
- travel to new places.
- connect with people on a deeper level.
- enjoy some much-deserved rest.

- find meaning and purpose doing the things that matter most to you.

Approaching the rest of your life with a beginning mindset is *key* to starting strong. Like a child who is curious about the world around them, always looking for a new adventure, you can view longevity with a sense of curiosity that can be a powerful factor in living your best life. This approach allows you to open a new chapter of aging with a healthy perspective and encouraging outlook. What a difference it can make moving forward!

Instead of having a fixed mindset—unyielding and immovable—you can develop a *growth* mindset that views the world as a place of limitless possibilities. With a best-is-yet-to-come attitude, you can create a new beginning right now.

A Purposeful Outlook

Former Olympic champion Jackie Joyner-Kersee once said, "Age is no barrier. It's a limitation you put on your mind."

While we can't will away our age, we *can* think differently about it. In fact, the sooner you adopt your personal Super Aging identity—an identity that is confident, enthusiastic, and purposeful—the sooner you can start living up to your greatest potential.

Are you starting to recognize the differences between the traditional mindset and the Super Aging mindset?

The old way goes something like this:

- *I've reached my final years. It's time to shut down and let others take the lead.*
- *I'm not able to do what I used to do, so I'll limit myself.*
- *I'm no longer able to contribute to society, so I guess I'm washed up and useless.*

In contrast, the Super Aging mindset goes like this:

- *I've reached a new season in life, and I can't wait to explore the new opportunities it will bring.*
- *I might not be able to do what I used to do, but I'm ready to learn new things.*
- *I'm a valuable member of society with a lot to offer. I'll make myself available to the younger generation.*

The Super Aging mindset views age as a friend instead of a foe. It determines to make the best of every situation and live with intentionality. As obstacles arise, you are less intimidated and more empowered to face them head-on. Instead of giving up, you'll move beyond your comfort zone and explore all your options.

Purpose is the *core* of the Super Aging mindset. It will propel you to plan your course and take small steps forward to make it happen. A purposeful mindset goes hand-in-hand with an attitude that says, "I get to."

A Get-To Attitude

When it comes to aging, there is often a depressing sense of *have to* instead of *get to*. That can lead to an unhealthy focus on merely surviving instead of thriving.

The Super Aging mindset flips this way of thinking on its head and says, "I look forward to the new opportunities retirement will provide, and I'm grateful for every new experience." The get-to mindset is one of positivity and excitement. It recognizes the new season for what it is and enthusiastically builds a new life structure.

According to a Boston University study published in 2019, researchers who tracked 70,000 men and women for 30 years and 10 years, respectively, "found that the most optimistic men and women demonstrated, on average, an 11–15% longer lifespan, and had far greater odds of reaching 85 years old, compared to the least optimistic group." [3]

Having an optimistic get-to vision of Super Aging is *key* to faithfully preserving your past, enhancing your present, and building a remarkable future.

> Having a get-to vision of Super Aging is key to faithfully preserving your past, enhancing your present, and building a remarkable future.

Let's paint an architectural word picture to drive this point home:

- Your Super Aging foundation is built on your strength of character, ingenuity, and values.
- Your structure includes the basic necessities of life such as food, clothing, and shelter.
- Your drywall is your network of support such as friends, family, church, social circles, and advisors.
- Your roof is your covering of emotional, physical, and financial peace.
- Your final touches are your years of enjoying retirement, experiencing amazing things, and living your best life.

The get-to mindset looks forward to building a new life full of hope and promise. Even when obstacles arise, you'll feel empowered to push through, which leads us to the next key in our Super Aging mindset.

A Fortitude Mentality

Typically, *mindset* is defined as "a mental attitude or belief about what is." For the Super Ager, attitudes and beliefs are grounded in a sense of fortitude that courageously believes the best—even in the face of adversity or loss.

A 70-year-old senior once shared about a terrifying caving experience that challenged her to either move forward or remain stuck.

Here's what she recalled:

> Naively, I thought going on a caving expedition in the Ardennes Mountains was going to be one of leisurely fun and easy exploration. I imagined our Belgian guides would lead us through wide-open caverns while we snapped pictures with our disposable cameras and stopped to admire the view. Imagine my surprise when the guides pointed to a hole in the ground—a hole with freezing water running into it—and said, "This is where we enter the cave."
>
> I remember laughing nervously, along with the other seniors in the group, and wondering if it was some sort of joke. It wasn't. Not only did we squeeze into that small hole in the ground, getting soaked in the process, we landed in a series of underground spaces that would take more than four hours to get through. Several times, we were stuck in narrow tunnels on our hands and knees, one after the other, while our guides went ahead to find the way out. I specifically remember thinking, I have two choices: I can either move forward bit by bit until I see daylight, or I can remain trapped underground with nowhere to go. I decided my only option was to have a mindset of fortitude and keep going. Looking back, it's one of the greatest adventures I've ever experienced and I'm glad I persevered. It's the same way I feel about age—press onward and upward with a fortitude mentality. And you know what? It's made a world of difference!

A mindset of fortitude will help you courageously face aging no matter how trapped you feel. It will push you to consistently trek forward until you reach your next goal. This mentality will help you make the next best decision every single time. Life's unexpected twists and turns will still happen, but you'll be *flexible* enough to navigate through them, and that's another element of the Super Aging mindset.

A Flexible Frame of Mind

Flexibility is difficult for many retirees because it's human nature to want to plan everything out and implement it flawlessly. Maintaining flexibility during your seasoned years is *key* to helping you steer around obstacles rather than seeing them as insurmountable barriers.

Here are a few examples of the flexible mindset:

- When an unexpected financial crisis hits, don't panic. Plan.
- When a health issue arises, don't give up. Fight.
- When relationships fail, find new relationships to enhance your journey.
- When retirement isn't what you thought it would be, make it what you *want* it to be.

Flexibility and resilience help you expand your horizons and explore different options. Remember, there's always more than one way of doing things. If a life event takes a sharp turn in the wrong direction, you have the power to grab the wheel and turn around.

Developing a flexible mindset is *key* to maintaining a "can-do" outlook. It allows you to yield when needed, stop to reevaluate, and steer your life in the direction you've planned. It also dispels doubt and moves you toward *empowerment*.

The Empowered Mind

Ultimately, the Super Aging mindset is about moving from fear to empowerment. While this doesn't come naturally, you can develop it through consistent, intentional attitudes and actions.

But before we get into the practical applications of the empowered mindset, let's look at some of the most common fears that come with aging:

- Fear of being alone
- Fear of outliving your savings
- Fear of being forced out of your home

- Fear of losing independence
- Fear of ongoing health issues
- Fear of not having the proper support network
- Fear of lacking purpose in life
- Fear of losing a loved one
- Fear of change and the unknown

These are *real* fears that deserve *real* consideration. However, with a Super Aging mindset, you can turn fears into plans—action plans—with a sense of purpose and empowerment. May I repeat that?

With a Super Aging mindset, you can turn fears into plans—action plans—with a sense of purpose and empowerment.

It's like pro mountain climber Matt Lloyd who found himself in a precarious situation on a literal wall of ice in Vail, Colorado. Here's what he said about this harrowing experience:

> I had never experienced anything like this, and there was noth-ing I could do to stop the shaking. I knew I had to control it or there would be fatal consequences. After what seemed like an eternity, I began taking deep breaths and forcefully exhaling the air to try and take command of the sinking ship that was my nervous system. It started working, and a plan took shape. I focused my mind on small, specific tasks.[4]

Matt's mindset—focusing on small, specific tasks—is what got him through that near-death experience. And when it comes to your retire-ment mindset, it's an attitude of empowerment that will help you focus on small, specific goals.

You *can* handle each challenge that comes along with peace of mind and clarity. Even when the unexpected happens, you can remain calm, cool, and collected. You might need to revisit your Plan B or come up with Plan C, but overall, you'll be able to examine each situa-tion with an attitude of strength and empowerment.

16

For example, let's say you've been planning a once-in-a-lifetime vacation, and you finally have the funds to go. You buy your plane ticket, plan for lodging and meals, research what to expect when you get there, and happily leave for your destination. However, some of these unexpected events might come along and threaten to ruin your trip:

- Delayed flights
- Missed connections
- Travel-related illness
- Unmet expectations
- Cancelled events

All these things are possible, and some actually come to pass, but instead of letting them ruin your vacation, reevaluate things, and adjust your trip. Once you've solved the problem, you can go back to having fun on your vacation. *That* is the perfect Super Aging mindset. An unexpected event doesn't thwart your trip, and it doesn't ruin your retirement. It redirects you; it points you to something different that might be even more rewarding.

> *"When we are no longer able to change a situation, we are challenged to change ourselves."*
> —Victor E. Frankl

Super Aging starts with mindset. Your way of thinking will make all the difference in the world. And as you change your mindset, you'll move forward with clarity and purpose. You will cross every bridge that stands between you and your destination with confidence and determination.

Consider these empowering affirmations for your journey:

- For every problem, there is more than one solution.

- Taking one step in the right direction is the best step to take.
- Your possibilities are endless!
- This is a wonderful season of life—embrace it!

Keep in mind that a Super Aging mindset isn't about avoiding your true feelings and emotions. It's addressing them, validating them, and redirecting them from fear to empowerment.

Here are some practical tips to help you develop a mindset of empowerment:

1. For each decision, write down the pros and cons. Examine them objectively.
2. Research your options. Ask for guidance. Engage with legal, financial, and elder care professionals.
3. Discuss your thoughts and plans with trusted friends or family members.
4. Sleep on every decision. Avoid making abrupt decisions that are emotionally charged.
5. Move forward with the next right step—no matter how small.
6. Stop and reevaluate things anytime you hit a roadblock.
7. Practice optimism. Believe it will all work out for the best.
8. Have the drive to do what others won't. Wishful thinking won't make things happen—action will.

Although we'll talk more about your physical well-being in the next chapter, it's worth mentioning that your physical habits and routines have a major impact on your mindset. If unhealthy habits consume most of your waking hours, you won't be able to handle the mental challenges that come your way. If, on the other hand, you're paying attention to living a healthy lifestyle, you'll find the Super Aging mindset far easier to develop.

Here's the bottom line. Your mindset is a culmination of attitudes and beliefs. Rather than allowing your emotions or circumstances to dictate your destiny, you can develop a purposeful outlook, a get-to attitude, and a flexible frame of mind that takes you from fear to empowerment.

You can turn that pivotal *uh-oh* moment about aging into a life-time of empowerment that says, "Watch out world. Here I come!"

Recap

Super Agers . . .

- Rise above the traditional way of thinking about age and develop a Super-Aging mindset.
- Approach retirement as a new beginning instead of an ending, the *key* to starting strong and finishing well.
- Adopt a personal Super Aging identity that is confident, enthusiastic, and purposeful to live up to their fullest potential.
- Have a get-to attitude that leads to thriving instead of merely surviving.
- Believe the best—even in the face of adversity—and move forward with a sense of courage and fortitude.
- Maintain flexibility to help steer around obstacles rather than seeing them as insurmountable barriers.
- Develop an empowered mindset that comes through consistent, intentional attitudes and actions.

The Super Aging Health & Wellness Lifestyle: Achieving Better Health for a Better You

What is called genius is the abundance of life and health.
—Henry David Thoreau

*This chapter contains health and wellness information that is meant to encourage and inform. However, please consult with your physician before engaging in any health, wellness, diet, or exercise plan.

Trillions—that's the number of dollars being spent in the health and wellness industry every year. And that number is expected to grow. Millions of people all over the world are exercising more, eating better, making healthier choices, and taking care of themselves like never before.

If you've ever done a Google search on the phrase "health and wellness," it's obvious there's no shortage of diet plans, fitness programs, nutritional supplements, and anti-aging products for this booming industry. Maintaining physical and mental health is important to people—whether they're 40 or 80.

Despite all of this, chronic disease (much of which is preventable) continues to be a growing epidemic in America. Nearly 80% of people over the age of 70 have one or more chronic conditions.

Small, healthy gains are instrumental in slowing the progression of age-related diseases and making the steady ascent toward optimal health. But let's look beyond these methods and programs. Becoming a Super Ager is about having the right perspective, developing a promising plan of action, and following through with healthy habits. Let me repeat that.

Becoming a Super Ager is about having the right perspective, developing a promising plan of action, and following through with healthy habits.

The important thing to remember when incorporating healthy habits into your lifestyle is to start small and give yourself enough time to make them a regular part of your routine. According to one study, the amount of time it takes for something to become a habit ranges from 18 to 254 days, with an average of 66 days.[1]

Take action for your health and well-being, but don't rush the process. Remember, a lifestyle is a way of living, not something you do intermittently or temporarily.

The Super Aging Health & Wellness Lifestyle focuses on the whole person—mind, body, and soul—and encourages people to start a wellness plan at any age or stage. So whether you are in your 40s, 50s, 70s, or 80s, this is a solid plan for a steady ascent to optimal health and wellness.

Before we jump into the action steps, let's take a short quiz to see where your starting point is.

Starting Point Health & Wellness Quiz

Read the following statements and rate yourself on a scale of 1–10.

1= highly **disagree**   10 = highly **agree**

1. _____ Your body is slowing down, and you believe there is nothing you can do to stop it.

2. _____ You've had health issues for years and assume you will have them the rest of your life.

3. _____ You are afraid of getting Alzheimer's disease.

4. _____ You struggle to lose weight and have given up the fight.

5. _____ You lack motivation for physical exercise.

6. _____ You rely on substances (alcohol, cigarettes, junk food) to help you cope.

7. _____ You find yourself too busy to invest in your health.

8. _____ You believe you have to join a gym or expensive diet program to be healthy.

9. _____ You believe genetics will ultimately determine your lifespan.

10. _____ You doubt most doctors and rely on Internet searches instead.

_____ TOTAL

Tally up your scores and read about your starting point below.

Score of 80–100

Your thoughts about health and wellness seem to be rooted in beliefs that could end up sabotaging your retirement years. The good thing is that your answers indicate you are a determined person, which is a great quality. Consider using some of that determination to develop a Super Aging mindset (see Chapter Two), and approach your health from the perspective of a promising future. You *can* adopt the Super Aging Health & Wellness Lifestyle. It is in *your* power to decide!

Score of 60–79

Your beliefs about health and wellness lean toward traditional thinking and may be limiting you as you enter retirement. However, your answers indicate you are open to change. By reevaluating your beliefs through the Super Aging lens, you'll find that some of your assumptions aren't as true as you thought. With a renewed dedication to change, you'll soon be on the Super Aging Health & Wellness track. You are on the verge of a breakthrough!

Score of 40–59

You seem to be standing on middle ground when it comes to your health and wellness. You're not sure what to believe, and understandably so. But don't be discouraged. You are in a great position to investigate the wonderful opportunity to adopt the Super Aging Health & Wellness Lifestyle. The following action steps will help clarify what it means to be the healthiest version of you and steer you in the right direction. You've got this!

Score of 20–39

When it comes to health and wellness, you seem to be open-minded and ready to explore new ways of doing things. That's great news! As you examine your attitudes and habits, you'll be more inclined to make the changes needed to incorporate the Super Aging Health & Wellness Lifestyle. Keep reading to start your action plan today. You are headed for success!

Score of 10–19

Wow! Your answers indicate you've managed to avoid the traditional mindset about aging in favor of an empowered mindset. Bravo! Your strong starting point will give you a head start on the Super Aging Health & Wellness track. As you read through the following action points, you'll be even better equipped to invest in your wellness journey. You are awesome!

No matter what your score was, even if you scored in the 80–100 range, you are only a few steps away from changing your life. As we emphasized earlier, "Your next first step is your best step." So be encouraged today—your journey to better health and wellness begins now!

One thing to consider as you move forward: Try to think of age as *biological* instead of *chronological*. After all, a number is just a number. Your actual age in years doesn't hinder your ability to live and move as if you were much younger. Don't let another birthday signal an automatic decline in your health. Celebrate the opportunity to start your Super Aging Health & Wellness Lifestyle and live your best life at any age.

Begin with Your Brain—the Powerhouse That Drives Everything

The term *brain health* can be confusing. People typically associate cognitive abilities in older adults as purely genetic. What people don't realize is that genetics aren't the only determiner of brain health. It's been proved over and over again that a person's lifestyle habits either build connective pathways for further cognitive and mental development or hinder brain pathways and lead to a cognitive and mental decline.

Your brain is the powerhouse that drives every system in your body. An unhealthy brain can lead to a breakdown of your body's ability to perform at optimal levels. I can't emphasize enough how important it is to pay close attention to your brain health.

According to healthybrains.org, "Your brain is a three pound universe that processes 70,000 thoughts each day using 100 billion neurons that connect at more than 500 trillion points through synapses that travel 300 miles/hour."[2]

Whew!

This miraculous organ governs your thoughts and emotions and regulates all your body's systems. That's why taking good care of your brain is essential to the Super Aging lifestyle. Here are a few key things you can do to ensure you are protecting, exercising, and expanding your brain health.

Stay Hydrated

The U.S. National Academies of Sciences, Engineering, and Medicine determined that an adequate daily fluid intake is:

About 15.5 cups (3.7 liters) of fluids a day for men
About 11.5 cups (2.7 liters) of fluids a day for women[3]

Without proper hydration, your "brain cells cannot function properly, leading to cognitive problems."[4]

If you struggle to get your daily intake of water, here are a few practical tips:

- Drink a glass of water before and after every meal.
- Add fruit (fresh or frozen) to your water for an added boost of flavor.
- Set a timer, and drink a full glass of water every two hours.

This basic yet important habit is vital to brain and body health. Do your best to stay hydrated.

Manage Stress

Chronic stress is no joke. Stress causes physical problems such as headaches, indigestion, sleeping difficulties, anxiety, social withdrawal, and fatigue. Not only does it have a negative effect on your attitude and actions, it has a negative effect on your brain functions. If you've ever experienced fuzzy thinking, brain fog, or bouts of anxiety, it could be an adverse effect of chronic stress. Mood, memory, depression, and other brain functions are reactive to stress and can cause all kinds of unwanted physical issues if left untreated.

Here are a few helpful tips for destressing:

- Yoga
- Prayer and meditation
- Journaling
- Massage

- Laughter
- Window shopping
- An evening out with friends
- A hike in the mountains
- Pampering yourself

Relaxation techniques take time to perfect, so be patient with yourself as you start new habits.

Monitor Your Numbers

Anytime your body is out of balance, it can have a negative impact on your health. That's why it's important to maintain regular check-ups and blood work to ensure your body is operating at full capacity. Closely monitor your cholesterol, your blood pressure, and your blood sugar. Talk with your doctor about healthy lifestyle options that will keep your numbers within the normal range and help you live your best life at any age.

Expand Your Thinking

Today is the perfect time to start exercising your brain in new ways. Grab those crosswords, sudokus, and jigsaw puzzles. Consider taking a college class, learning a new language or computer program, taking dance lessons, playing online games, or starting a new hobby. From the comfort of your own home, you can access online learning programs such as Great Courses, Road Scholar, Coursera, and local college classes. Those activities will expand your thinking and exercise your brain—thus increasing your cognitive abilities.

Travel the World

Travel can be a major boost to brain health as you step out of your routines and experience new sights, sounds, and scenery—either close to home or far away. In fact, travel is at the top of the list for many Super Agers since they finally have time to leisurely explore new places. Cruises, senior bus tours, and motor coach vacations are ideal for aging adults who want to sit back, relax, and make new connections along the way.

Get Mental and Emotional Support

If you're consumed with the fear of getting dementia or other brain diseases, talk with a trusted doctor, counselor, or mental health professional. Be honest about your concerns, and follow their expert advice. Allowing your mind to dwell on things that may never happen will only cause mental and emotional anguish. Don't be afraid to reach out for support. In fact, the more support you have, the better.

Another factor in boosting your mental health is resisting isolation. This is easier said than done, especially in light of the recent COVID-19 pandemic and the heavy toll it took on all of us. However, loneliness and isolation are major contributors to depression, anxiety, and emotional instability. Resist the temptation to self-isolate. Connect with others whenever possible, even if it's online through platforms such as Skype, FaceTime, or Zoom. Relating to others in meaningful ways is a major contributor to your mental and emotional health.

Get Moving

Heart, lungs, organs, muscles, and tendons—every part of your body needs an ample supply of oxygen. The boost of oxygen that comes from physical exercise is vital in order for your body systems to thrive and keep thriving as you age.

You don't have to run a marathon (unless you want to) to get more oxygen into your body. According to experts, "Breathing exercises are extremely effective in improving oxygenation. Yogic breathing also referred to more descriptively as diaphragmatic breathing or the Sanskrit form "pranayama" improve your oxygen intake by focusing on using your key respiratory muscle (the diaphragm) to take in deeper inhales and longer exhales releasing a greater volume of carbon dioxide."[5]

One of the simplest ways to get the oxygen flowing is to walk more. Walking is one of the most fundamental ways you can increase mobility and incorporate movement into your routine.

Here are a few more "get moving" ideas that can easily be incorporated into your daily or weekly routine:

- Start your morning with a few warm-up exercises as your coffee brews. Do some squats, yoga poses, or walking in place.
- Join a gym or fitness program such as Silver Sneakers with more than 17,000 locations and even online classes.[6]
- Find an activity you love, and make time for it every week. Develop activities you can do for a lifetime—even in your 80s and 90s—such as swimming, pickleball, and bicycling.
- Enlist an exercise buddy to take walks with you, lift weights, or go on hikes. (Everything's better with a friend!)

If you think you're too old to incorporate a fitness routine, think again. "In 2013, at 80 years old, Yuchiro Miura became the oldest person to summit Mount Everest. Despite battling diabetes, undergoing three heart surgeries, and recovering from a complicated operation to repair his shattered pelvis in the decade between the summit attempts . . . he persisted, rebuilding his fitness routine until he was ready to tackle the penultimate peak once more."[7]

While cardio is essential for overall health, it's also important to incorporate strength training into your weekly routine. Weightlifting, resistance training, push-ups, sit-ups, and squats—these exercises help with flexibility, agility, and balance. They are especially beneficial for aging adults who want to remain strong and independent. The key is to make physical fitness part of your weekly routine—without excuse.

Remember, as the old saying goes, you're either moving forward or making excuses. You can't do both. When it comes to new habits and goals, consider the advice of James Clear, author of *Atomic Habits*. "New goals don't deliver new results. New lifestyles do. And a lifestyle is not an outcome, it's a process. For this reason, all of your energy should go into building better habits, not chasing better results."

> "New goals don't deliver new results. New lifestyles do. And a lifestyle is not an outcome, it's a process. For this reason, all of your energy should go into building better habits, not chasing better results."
> —James Clear, Atomic Habits

Remember, you are never too old to get moving! And while physical exercise is a big part of the Super Aging Health & Wellness Lifestyle, it doesn't have to be a drudgery. I encourage you to view movement as a blessing. Begin each day with gratitude that you are able to move your body and keep your systems working properly.

Add More Healthy Stuff

One key element of becoming a Super Ager is to view health improvements as *empowering* instead of *limiting*. That creates a mindset of abundance instead of deprivation. By adding more healthy stuff, you'll automatically drop the bad stuff and begin to crave healthier habits.

If your diet consists of mostly processed foods, start by adding one fresh fruit and one vegetable each day. Increase those amounts gradually until you are eating mostly whole foods with occasional junk-food indulgences.

Diets such as the MIND Diet or Mediterranean Diet encourage "the consumption of all kinds of vegetables, berries, nuts, olive oil, whole grains, fish, beans, poultry and a moderate amount of wine."[8] Minimize the consumption of red meats, butter, margarine, dairy, pastries, sweets, and fried foods. Healthier diets can extend longevity and prevent loss of brain function as you age.

THE MIND DIET

What is the Mind Diet? The Mind Diet combines elements of both the Mediterranean and Dash Diets that have shown to be beneficial for the brain.

TEN HEALTHY FOOD GROUPS

WHOLE GRAINS	BERRIES	CHICKEN OR TURKEY
3X DAILY	2X A WEEK	2X A WEEK

DARK LEAFY GREENS AND VEGGIES	BEANS	WINE
1X DAILY	EVERY OTHER DAY	5 OZ. GLASS DAILY

FISH	NUTS	OLIVE OIL
AT LEAST 1X A WEEK	1 OZ. DAILY	PRIMARY COOKING OIL

FOOD TO KEEP TO A MINIMUM

FAST FOOD	RED MEAT	FRIED FOOD	PASTRIES & SWEETS

BUTTER & MARGARINE	CHEESE

Look for natural, organic foods and spices that contain anti-aging benefits and reduce inflammation. Some herbs such as turmeric, cumin, and ginger are known to lower blood pressure. Other spices such as cinnamon and rosemary can help stabilize blood sugar and may prevent diabetes.[9]

In addition to choosing natural food options, there are a few more things to add to your abundant Health & Wellness Lifestyle.

- Spend 5–10 minutes a day in quiet prayer or meditation.
- Try a few relaxation techniques such as yoga, tai chi, or mindfulness.
- Spend more time with people you care about.
- Enjoy creative outlets such as painting, going to concerts, or visiting a local farmers market.
- Make sure you are getting enough vitamin D and sensible sun exposure.

Look at becoming a Super Ager as a way to add beauty to your life. Resist limiting beliefs that cause you to hold back. Embrace empowering beliefs that propel you forward.

Get the Best Rest

Not sleeping well? Don't assume "it's just how it is." Quality sleep is essential to your health and well-being. Without it, you'll be at risk of developing adverse issues such as brain fog, moodiness, susceptibility to illness, and weight gain.

Problems with insomnia, restless leg syndrome, and sleep apnea—all common among older adults—make it harder to feel rested. However, there are a few simple things you can do to get a better night's sleep and wake up ready for life's adventures.

Establish a sleep schedule. Try to get to bed at the same time each night and wake up at the same time each morning. Establishing a predictable sleep routine can help set your internal clock and improve the quality of your sleep during those hours.

Stay cool. Research shows that staying cool promotes better sleep. Although the ideal room temperature is 70–74 degrees Fahrenheit during the day, the ideal temperature drops to 60–67 degrees Fahrenheit at night. Programming your thermostat to drop a few degrees at bedtime, wearing lightweight night clothes, opening windows, and using breathable bedding can help you stay cool at night and get better rest.

Avoid or limit sleeping during the day. Napping is not the root of all evil, but it *can* interfere with a good night's sleep. Sometimes, a nap is just what the doctor ordered, but 20–30 minutes should suffice, and morning naps tend to be better than afternoon naps.

Dedicate your bed to sleep. Spending too much time in bed doing recreational activities such as watching TV, working, doing crossword puzzles, and scrolling on your phone can confuse your body clock. If you go to bed only when it's time to sleep, your brain will begin to associate your bedroom with tiredness and rest.

These quick and easy suggestions can improve sleep at any age. If sleep is an issue for you, consider reaching out to your doctor and scheduling a sleep study. This is one area of your health you can and should work to improve and then enjoy the lasting results.

Create Your "Dream Team"

With the explosion of Internet searches, people have taken their health into their own hands. Occasional Internet research does come in handy, but most people get lost on virtual rabbit trails that concoct all sorts of possible medical conditions—some that are rather frightening.

Instead of relying on the Internet to diagnose yourself, enlist a trusted medical doctor, nutritionist, personal fitness instructor, or emotional support professional to work with you to determine your best course of action. Create your "dream team" of experts as part of your personal support system.

Think of your dream team as your partners in accountability who hold you responsible for your habits and beliefs. With modern technology, many chronic diseases can be prevented or delayed. You just need the right team of people on your side who are committed to offering preventative screenings and support. Choose people who align with your beliefs and will join you on your journey to wellness.

Here are some things to look for in a trusted professional:

- They listen more than they speak, not rushing you out the door.
- They work with you to find the best, personalized solutions.
- They help you eliminate unnecessary prescriptions in favor of natural supplements.
- They are easily accessible.
- They inspire you, encourage you, and have those tough conversations when necessary.
- They stay up-to-date on the latest health trends and are willing to discuss them with you.

In addition to your support team, there are also ways to monitor your health by using the latest technology. Consider investing in an Apple Watch, Fitbit, pulse oximeter, or app to track your steps, calories, heart rate, and more. If you are *really* ambitious, you might want to consider getting a Peloton, a popular indoor bike that includes membership plans for competitive workouts and studio classes from the comfort of your home.

Think Longevity

Longevity isn't a word we throw around in everyday conversation, but perhaps it's time to start. The term means "long life," and long life, after all, is a wonderful thing—especially when it's vibrant and healthy.

You've probably heard that 70 is the new 50 and that people are living "younger" than ever.

As more generations live to the age of 100, also known as *centenarians*, there will be more discoveries of commonalities that contribute to their longevity. We'll continue to learn more about attitudes, habits, and behaviors that encompass these real-life Super Agers, things like these:

- Living with a sense of purpose
- Staying optimistic
- Minimizing stress
- Incorporating physical exercise
- Connecting with others

Nir Barzilai, M.D., founding director of the Institute for Aging Research at Albert Einstein College of Medicine, has studied the "biology of aging, including the biological effects of nutrients on extending life and the genetic determinants of life span."[10] His belief is that conventional aging can be altered and even greatly delayed by discovering unique longevity genes in centenarians and their children. By targeting these people's health spans (the part of a person's life when they are in good health), Barzilai hopes to improve the quality of life for seniors everywhere.

Remember, your physical health and well-being are important, but that entails a whole lot more than diet and exercise. No matter where your starting point is, you can take small, incremental steps toward brain health, better habits, good sleep, and a strong support network. After all, you are worth it!

How will you implement what you've learned in this chapter? What will be your first steps toward better health and a better you?

Recap

Super Agers . . .

- Develop a promising plan of action and follow through with healthy habits.
- Focus on the whole person—mind, body, and soul.
- Think of age as *biological* instead of *chronological* since biological age can be much younger than a person's actual age.
- View health improvements as empowering instead of limiting. By adding more good stuff, they automatically drop most of the bad stuff.

Super Aging Relationships:
Staying Connected during Retirement

If you live to be a hundred, I want to live to be a hundred minus one day so that I never have to live without you.

—Winnie the Pooh

Research professor and author Brené Brown says, "We are wired for connection. It's in our biology. From the time we are born, we need connection to thrive emotionally, physically, spiritually, and intellectually." Her words remind us that connection is key to living a full and happy life. Without interpersonal contact, we are void of one of the most fundamental aspects of thriving.

The world has become a much smaller place, especially with the rise of social media and its ability to link people like never before. However, maintaining meaningful social connections as we get older isn't as easy as we might think. Many older adults find themselves with shrinking circles of family and friends, which can leave a noticeable void. The result is loneliness, and that can become a major strain on a person's emotional and physical health.

Super Agers view relationships as one of the most important driving factors of happiness during retirement. They proactively surround themselves with people who make them feel loved, valued, and accepted. They engage in thought-provoking discussions that stretch their thinking and provide healthy interaction. Most importantly, Super Agers *invest* in their relationships as though they were the most valuable assets on earth.

In this chapter, we'll discuss the common pain points in our relationships and offer genuine ways to stay connected during retirement.

Find Deeper Happiness with Your Spouse

Research indicates that happiness in marriage leads to longevity. That's because marriage provides camaraderie unlike any other relationship. It provides a sense of comfort and security, a oneness designed from the beginning of creation.

Too many retirees fail to see the importance of marital happiness as a key to a rich and fulfilling life. They take for granted the one person who has always been there. They overlook the powerful teamwork and support their spouse can provide.

A Super Ager sees their spouse as their better half, always considering their needs and desires above their own. These husbands and wives realize the irreplaceable value of their spouses and make them a number-one priority.

Gerontologist and Cornell University professor Karl Pillemer interviewed hundreds of retirees about the secret of a happy marriage. The retirees unanimously agreed that "your relationship with your spouse has to come before the kids, in-laws, jobs, friends and everything else."[1]

Too often, we grow comfortable in marriage and inadvertently move our spouse to the bottom of our priority list. They get our leftovers at the end of the day rather than our best time and attention. If this is a common issue in your marriage, consider these practical ways to find deeper happiness with your spouse:

- Listen more than you've ever listened.
- Encourage your spouse often, and affirm their ideas.
- Bite your tongue, and let trivial things go.
- Know when to give them space without feeling wounded by it.
- Communicate about everything (and nothing).
- Turn off your phone in their presence.
- Give a gift just because.

- Incorporate more physical touch without the expectation of sex.
- Ease some of their burdens by taking on some of the responsibilities.
- Have friendly competitions.
- Laugh (a lot)!

If you find yourself in a rough patch in your marriage due to financial strain, communication problems, or unresolved issues, reach out to a trusted counselor or relationship coach. Commit to tackling your issues *immediately* to prevent a root of bitterness from rising up.

Happiness in marriage can lead to a longer, more fulfilling life. Nurture your relationship with the utmost care and undivided attention, and watch for deeper happiness and contentment.

Have Friends You Can Count On

Super Agers recognize that they've reached a stage in life where their grown kids are busy with their own families and careers, many of their former coworkers are still working 9 to 5, and their online friendships are barely scratching the surface of real connectivity. And thus they seek out true and lasting friendships—friendships they can count on.

There's a proverb that says, "There is a friend who sticks closer than a brother," and it's that kind of friend that Super Agers need most during retirement.

Louis Cozolino, professor of psychology at Pepperdine University, says, "How we bond and stay attached to others is at the core of our resilience, self-esteem, and physical health. We build the brains of our children through our interaction with them, and we keep our own brains growing and changing throughout life by staying connected to others." [2]

A person doesn't need a multitude of friends to experience the benefits that Cozolino describes. In fact, a few "deeper" friendships are more important than dozens of superficial ones that fail to meet our inner desire for lasting connection. It's those few, faithful friends who will walk with us through every hardship, celebrate our wins—big and small—and be trusted confidants as we journey through life.

ATTRIBUTES THAT HELP YOU CONNECT WITH OTHERS:

- Be vulnerable
- Be available
- Be trustworthy
- Listen well
- Ask questions
- Share your story

Whether you're cultivating old friendships or new ones, keep in mind that it's the deeper friendships that support your mental and physical well-being. But before we address the specific health benefits of meaningful friendships, let's talk about relationships that aren't so beneficial.

Psychologist Andrea Bonior, Ph.D. notes, "With self-reflection and increased wisdom comes the realization that we really should maximize the number of good relationships we have and not spend so much time on the ones that aren't good."[23]

While it might be hard to imagine ending a friendship, it's sometimes necessary to evaluate the benefits versus the drawbacks of a relationship. Here are some comparative questions to ask yourself when you decide if a friendship is worth continuing:

- After spending time with them, do you find yourself energized or depleted?
- Do they regularly build you up or constantly tear you down?
- Are they mostly positive or mostly negative?
- Can you depend on them, or are they unreliable and wishy-washy?

- Do you trust them, or have they given you reason to distrust them?
- Do they keep you focused on a painful past or propel you toward a purposeful future?

These questions might be difficult to answer, so give yourself plenty of time to contemplate them. If any of your friendships continuously lean toward the negative, it might be wise to reevaluate that relationship.

On the flip side, spending time with *true* friends can actually benefit your mental and physical health. More and more studies are showing that deeper social connection can lower the risk of heart attacks, reduce blood pressure, and protect against cognitive decline. More results of engaging with trusted friends are less stress, anxiety, and depression.[4]

Super Agers choose friends who contribute to their overall well-being. They seek out like-minded people who are encouragers instead of discouragers. They invest in people who listen well, ask thoughtful questions, bring out the best in them, and are dependable day or night. They value friends who "stick closer than a brother" and make them a priority.

Stay connected during retirement by finding your tribe—no matter how small. Then spend the majority of your time and energy with those people. Your mental and physical health may very well depend on it!

Single? Date with Confidence

Single retirees who want to date again often find themselves in a predicament. They've lived long enough to know what type of person they're looking for, but they've also lived long enough to know that the dating scene has changed dramatically.

Here's a bit of trivia about dating throughout the years:

1960s: Group dating was the best way to meet that special someone in hopes of going steady.

1970s: Personal newspaper ads advertised people seeking love and companionship. Women described their physical attributes while men boasted of financial security.

1980s: Receiving a mixtape was a good sign that someone wanted to go out with you. The blinking light on the answering machine became an obsession.

1990s: Face-to-face meet-ups at restaurants and bars were all the rage. If you were really lucky, you had a song dedicated to you on Friday night radio.

2000s: Burning CDs and talking on pay-as-you-go flip phones were the dating highlights.

Today: Online dating sites have swept the globe and are used by more than 30 million people nationwide.[5]

There's no argument that dating has changed a lot over the years, and many retirees aren't sure where to begin. Whether you decide to dip your toe into online dating or stick to more traditional ways of interacting, here are a few key things to help you date with confidence.

1. Reboot after Divorce

With the rise of divorce among older adults, it's important to take time to reboot before stepping into the world of dating. That will allow you to settle into a new routine, discover things about yourself you didn't know before, and allow necessary healing to take place.

Resist rebound dating since it will likely lead to a sense of disappointment and disillusionment. Allow yourself time to reset by taking a vacation, spending time with kids and grandkids, relocating if needed, and settling into your new life as a single person. Once you've had time to rediscover what makes you "you," you'll be better prepared to explore new relationships.

2. Establish What Works for You and What Doesn't

It's imperative to establish things that are non-negotiable for you. That might include a person's religious beliefs, financial security, interactions with family members, and trustworthiness. Seriously consider what kind of person will be the most compatible, and don't settle for just anyone. Here are a few things you'll want to consider:

- Do you share similar goals? If your retirement plans don't match, there's no sense pursuing the relationship any further. It will only lead to two very unhappy people trying to merge two different lifestyles.
- Do conversations come easily, or are there frequent, awkward silences? It's normal upon first meeting to have a few awkward moments, but if things don't smooth out over time, chances are the communication won't improve.
- Is the person dependable? Can you count on them to do what they say they'll do? You must be able to trust them and count on them to be there no matter what.
- How do they interact with others, especially family members? If the person you're dating is constantly engaging in family drama, you might want to reconsider the relationship. After all, you don't want their relationship issues to become *your* relationship issues.
- Are they happy? Easy going? Compatible? The retirement years should be fun years. If someone is constantly bringing you down, think about what that will look like for the long haul.
- Are their finances in order, or would you be walking into a hot mess if the relationship continued? Financial security is a must for relationships during retirement. That doesn't mean the

43

other person has to be wealthy, but they do need to be self-sufficient and have their finances in order.

Super Agers know what works for them and what doesn't, and they're not afraid to stick to the lifestyle standards they've set. So if you're going to explore the dating world, establish your key "musts" up-front, and move forward with confidence.

3. Expect It to Take Time

Patience needs to be your close companion when dating during retirement. Not only will this help you resist rushing into the wrong relationship, but it will help you maintain a sense of peace in the process.

Ken was in his late 60s before he finally figured out the benefit of patience. After dating the wrong people for several years, he finally met his perfect match through an online dating site. She was completely different than anyone he'd ever dated, but because he hadn't rushed the process, he ended up with the one meant for him. He now advises other retirees to "be willing to stick with it for as long as it requires."[6]

Super Agers are not only patient, they are diligent, consistent, and clear-headed. They take a "leisurely stroll" approach to dating instead of a "run-to-the-finish line" approach, which saves them from rushing into a volatile situation that doesn't turn out well. With confidence, they seek out relationships with realistic expectations and a sense of peace and calm.

4. Be Yourself

No matter how old we get, it's human nature to try to impress other people—especially when we first meet them. But finding the right companion in retirement requires you to be absolutely authentic from the start. Be exactly who you are—unapologetically.

There's something amazingly refreshing about a true blue person who has nothing to hide. And Super Agers are great at letting their true colors show. Not only will this build a solid foundation from the very beginning of your relationship, it will eliminate unexpected (and unwanted) surprises down the road.

5. Expand Your Horizons

If online dating sites intimidate you, look elsewhere. Expand your horizons by looking into church socials, community events, volunteer opportunities, gyms, YMCAs, and local senior meet-ups.

Yes, the dating scene is far different than it was 40 years ago. But single retirees have just as much opportunity to meet their special someone, first by establishing a few personal ground rules and then by being authentic and getting involved. You *can* date with confidence during retirement!

Balance the Relationship with Your Kids

Having a close relationship with your adult kids is both wonderful and rewarding. However, many retirees struggle to find a healthy balance in this area. The pendulum can swing from extreme over-involvement to complete detachment, leaving both parents and kids disillusioned in the process. Balancing this relationship is possible when you see things through a constructive lens of give and take.

Here are a few examples:

- Respect your generational differences while continuing your own tried-and-true ways of doing things.
- Visit your kids and grandkids regularly, but still live your life and enjoy your own activities.
- Help them financially—*only* if it's part of your retirement plan. Otherwise, find non-monetary ways to help out such as babysitting or helping with minor home or car repairs.
- Be a source of wisdom and advice, but accept the fact that you can't fix everything.
- Be respectful of their partner, even if you don't get along.

- Show interest in their careers, family life, and extracurricular activities while sharing your personal interests and endeavors.
- Get involved in joint hobbies and try things you never thought you'd try such as archery, golf, computer classes, or art lessons.
- Jump on social media to keep up with the younger generation. Your grandkids will think you're so cool when they see you engaging on TikTok or Instagram.
- Make holidays with family a priority, but don't feel guilty if you miss an occasional event.
- If there's tension between you and your adult children, give them some space. Then reach out to mend the gap before it grows too wide.

The interesting thing about getting older is that the longer parents live, the more they find they're aging together with their kids. In essence, the age gap narrows as time goes on, and kids find they have more in common with their parents than they thought.

Kathrin Boerner, gerontology professor at McCormack Graduate School at the University of Massachusetts, Boston, believes our parent-child bonds affect the last stages of our lives. "We're looking at a new phenomenon with longevity that was once almost freakish," she said. "More baby boomers still have their parents than any previous age cohort."[7]

With that in mind, make sure the relationship with your kids is well-balanced and enjoyable. Maintain a Super Aging perspective of healthy boundaries, good communication, and plenty of give and take.

Gift Your Grandchildren with the Best Kind of Gifts

This chapter wouldn't be complete without mentioning the importance of staying connected to our grandkids. My relationship with my grandmother made a profound impact on my life choices and eventually my career. Her influence was one of the most important influences

I've ever experienced, and she gifted me with invaluable traits such as compassion, faith, and integrity.

Gift your grandchildren with the best non-monetary gifts you can give, including your time, attention, wisdom, and example. Teach them what you know, and impress on them what you've learned. Be sure you're always there for them. Grandchildren are precious assets to our lives, and staying connected with them should be a top priority for every Super Ager. Find ways to spend quality time with your grand-kids, and leave behind an incredible legacy they'll never forget.

Honor Aging Parents

Years ago, families lived together and supported generations of loved ones under one roof. One person never felt the burden of taking care of an aging parent because there were plenty of others around to contribute.

Surprisingly, multigenerational homes are making a comeback as people are finding it easier to age together rather than support one another across the miles. But whether you decide to join this growing trend or not, remember that the most important thing about your parents is your relationship with them.

Part of the Super Aging mindset is being able to look beyond the surface and find deeper value in people. Instead of viewing aging parents as inconveniences, Super Agers focus on the legacy they've left. They recognize that their parents had a big influence on who they are—good or bad—and they're committed to honoring their aging parents with grace and dignity.

Here are a few things to consider when honoring your aging parents.

It starts with forgiveness.
Author and theologian Lewis B. Smedes once said, "To forgive is to set a prisoner free and discover that the prisoner was you."

Super Agers work hard to forgive past grievances, knowing that time is short and there might not be another chance to reconcile with their aging parents. This often involves honest conversations that aren't easy but necessary for the healing process. If you are struggling to forgive an aging parent, consider meeting with a trusted counselor, life coach, or friend to help bridge the gap and bring peace to the situation.

It involves time.

Retirement opens up our schedules and allows us to make time for the people we love. Often what matters most to our aging parents is time. All they want is our presence and a listening ear. Schedule regular time with them, and make a commitment to just "be there." It is one time commitment you won't regret.

It involves duty.

Author Kathryn Slattery says this about caring for her aging mother: "It didn't help when well-meaning friends would say, 'Oh, you're such a good daughter to be taking such good care of your mother.' No, I'm not, I wanted to say. If I were honest, I'd admit that much of what I do for my mother is more about duty than love."[8]

When the relationship between you and your aging parent feels more like duty, remember the sense of duty they must have had raising you. What was once their responsibility to care for and provide for you has now become your responsibility to care for them. The thing to remember is that it's only for a season, and "this, too, shall pass."

Make your aging parents a priority as you do the work to forgive past grievances, spend quality time with them, and do what it takes to care for them. In the end, you'll be able to look back with peace of mind that you did what you could to give them the honor they deserved.

Use Social Media for Connection, Not Distraction

What would a chapter on relationships be without the mention of social media? According to the Pew Research Center, at least 7 in 10

Americans use social media for connection, engagement, interaction, and entertainment.[9] The fastest growing segment of users on the Internet are over the age of 65, so it makes perfect sense that staying connected during retirement includes social media interaction.

But does social media really keep us stay connected, or does it keep us distracted? For retirees, the online space can play a big role in helping them feel included—especially with distant family members and longtime friends. Platforms such as Facebook, Twitter, and Instagram can greatly expand a retiree's online engagement and help them find fun ways to connect.

On the other hand, too much time on social media can diminish face-to-face interactions. With its addictive pull, many people—young and old—spend far too many hours mindlessly surfing the web instead of engaging with people in the physical world.

Here are a few signs that you might be distracted by social media:

- You find yourself anxious after checking your social media accounts.
- It's the thing you turn to when you feel lonely or sad.
- You'd rather connect online than in person.
- You avoid social outings in favor of online meetings or events.

If social media has become all-consuming, consider taking an extended break. During that time, look for social events in your community such as theater and concert performances, educational events at a local college or university, arts and craft shows, and senior events. As you incorporate social media back into your schedule, use it to promote healthy connections instead of unhealthy distractions.

As the world seems to grow smaller by the day, we are offered a multitude of ways to connect with people near and far. Making your relationships a priority during retirement will not only contribute to your health and well-being but will also become the most important driving factor of your retirement happiness.

Recap

Super Agers . . .

- View relationships as one of the most important driving factors of happiness during retirement. They proactively surround themselves with people who make them feel loved, valued, and accepted.
- Realize that a few deeper friendships are more important than dozens of superficial ones and that they contribute to their mental health and physical well-being.
- Know that happiness in marriage leads to longevity, and they should value their spouses and make them a number-one priority.
- Aren't afraid to explore the dating world and are good at establishing personal standards and moving forward with confidence.
- Create healthy boundaries with their kids and foster good communication along with plenty of give and take.
- Recognize that their parents had a big influence on who they are—good or bad—and are committed to honoring them with grace and dignity.
- Stay connected during retirement and include social media interaction without allowing it to replace face-to-face connections.

Super Aging Retirement Readiness: Preparing Your Finances for Retirement

*One secret of success in life is for a man to be ready
for his opportunity when it comes.*

—Benjamin Disraeli

Legendary coach John Wooden of the UCLA Bruins was con-sidered one of the greatest coaches of all time. With 10 national championships in 12 years, his success was largely attributed to two things—preparedness and discipline. One of his mottos was, "Do not let what you cannot do interfere with what you can do."

During retirement, many people feel limited when it comes to creating financial security for their future. They feel inadequately prepared to evaluate their finances and create a long-term financial plan to meet all their retirement needs. Ultimately, they aren't sure they've saved enough money to live comfortably for the remainder of their lives.

Super Agers, however, don't hide from reality, and they hope for the best. They certainly don't allow a lack of knowledge to halt their planning efforts. In fact, they feel empowered to gather all the information they need, analyze alternatives and options, find trusted advisors, create a plan, and diligently prepare for their future.

So where do *you* fall on the readiness meter?

Hopefully, you're learning everything you can for a better under-standing of what retirement entails. Perhaps you've met with a retirement planner to examine your portfolio and discuss future plans.

And maybe you have a written plan to achieve your financial goals and stay on track.

If you don't have these things in place, don't worry. We know there isn't always a clear-cut perfect time to retire since health issues, job displacement, and other factors sometimes force us to change direction when we transition to retirement.

Just know that wherever you are on the retirement timeline, you *can* do this! It's never too late to prepare for your future.

10 FINANCIAL QUESTIONS TO ASK YOURSELF BEFORE YOU RETIRE

1. Have you prepared a formal financial plan, including an income and investment strategy?

2. Is your monthly income sufficient to support your retirement lifestyle?

3. Have you achieved your savings goal, and can you survive a market downturn?

4. Have you planned for the effects of inflation and taxes on your long-term budget?

5. Do you have a six-month emergency fund for unexpected expenses?

6. Have you calculated the amount of Social Security benefits you'll receive at your planned retirement age?

7. Do you have adequate health insurance coverage?

8. Have you thought about working longer or starting an "encore career"?

9. Have you considered moving or downsizing your home?

10. Do you have a strategy to pay for long-term care expenses?

Below is a *Super Aging Retirement Readiness Meter* with five points to gauge your retirement readiness. From your current investments to your long-term legacy, you can measure what it will take for you to prepare successfully.

Don't leave your retirement planning to the experts or procrastinate any longer. Take the Super Ager approach by gathering all the information you need and putting that information into action. Progressively, you'll move the needle on your retirement readiness plan and find yourself more prepared than ever.

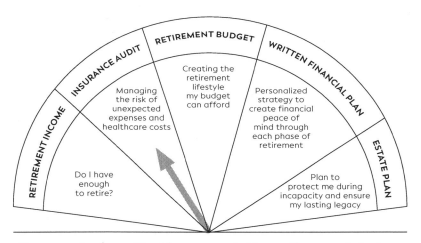

Super Aging Retirement Readiness Meter

The 5-Point Super Aging Retirement Readiness Meter

1. Income and Investment Analysis

Do you have enough money to retire?

If this question causes your palms to sweat and your heart to beat a little faster, you're not alone. Many people facing retirement take a fingers-crossed approach to their finances and avoid looking at the numbers. Super Agers, on the other hand, analyze every detail of their financial investments with eyes wide open.

The word *analyze* means "to examine something and determine its condition." The condition of your finances will likely determine when, where, and how you'll retire, so you'll need to carefully analyze all your income sources and investments. That includes Social Security benefits, individual retirement accounts (IRAs), 401(k) plans, real estate, stocks, bonds, mutual funds, and other investment assets.

Once you've determined the condition of your finances, you'll need to calculate how much you'll ideally need to save in order to retire comfortably and make your money last. On average, people spend $3,800 per month in retirement, provided they've paid off their mortgages and don't have outstanding debt. However, this number can vary greatly, depending on the lifestyle you're used to and the retirement lifestyle you're planning on.

If Social Security is your main source of income as it is for many seniors, there are a few things to keep in mind before collecting this benefit. While the minimum age to start collecting is 62, it might be beneficial to wait until you are at your full retirement age (based on the year you were born). There is a sizable increase in the monthly amount you'll receive if you wait until your full retirement age or until you turn 70, which increases the monthly amount by another 8%. If you have other reliable income sources or are still working, it would be to your best interest to wait to claim your Social Security benefits.

One rule of thumb for building your retirement fund and making it last is the 4% rule. Basically, you should withdraw no more than 4% from your retirement funds each year so you don't dip into your investment principle. Your retirement fund should last 30 years by making 4% annual withdrawals.

For example, if you plan on spending $50,000 per year during retirement, you'll need a savings of at least $1.25 million. Keep in mind that this doesn't take Social Security and other sources of income into account. You'll also need to factor in 3% for inflation each year and withdraw accordingly.

- If you're not sure how much money to save in order to live according to the 4% rule, here are three primary questions to ask yourself:
- What will your retirement expenses include?
- How long will your funds need to last?
- How much will you continue to earn on your investments?

Let's take a deeper look at these key questions.

What will your retirement expenses include?

According to Market Watch, retirees "usually spend more in their first five years of retirement than at other times, and then it begins to decline."[1] That's because in those first five years, people are crossing things off their bucket lists—traveling, finding their long-term home and community, pursuing things they've always wanted to pursue. While there's nothing wrong with those things (and many are a necessary part of the process), you need to plan for them financially. Other essential retirement expenses include housing, healthcare, taxes, food, transportation, entertainment, inflation, and emergencies.

Here's a simple, practical budgeting exercise that can help you determine your retirement expenses:

- Gather your bank and credit card statements for the last 12 months.
- Calculate your monthly and yearly income totals.
- Identify all recurring payments—monthly, quarterly, and yearly.
- Factor in the impact of income tax and inflation.
- Eliminate debt, unnecessary spending, and costly habits.
- Determine what your yearly retirement expenses will be based on your current income and recurring payments (minus the things you can eliminate today).

According to one wealth management company, most people believe that "after retirement, their annual spending will amount to only 70% to 80% of what they spent previously. Such an assumption is often proved to be unrealistic, especially if the mortgage has not been paid off or if unforeseen medical expenses occur."[2]

Don't underestimate your retirement expenses. Take into consideration your current standard of living, and be realistic about how you view your retirement years. It's better to be overprepared than underprepared.

How long will your funds need to last?

The longevity of your retirement savings will depend on various factors, including how long you plan to continue working, when you start receiving Social Security benefits, unforeseen medical and living expenses, inflation, and the returns you make on investments. While you can't predict every unforeseen expense, you can plan for 30+ years and stretch your retirement dollars over the span of your lifetime. Take a look at this three-step approach:

1. Budget for the unknowns. By having an adequate emergency fund (at least six months of expenses), you'll have a nice financial cushion. Designate this fund for things such as unexpected home or car repairs and family and medical emergencies. Just be sure to replenish it as soon as possible after dipping into it.

2. Reduce costs as you go. There are certain expenses that are necessary during your working years—mortgages, college loans, and so on—that you may not have in your retirement years. Review your budget regularly, and nix expenses that are no longer applicable to your Super Aging lifestyle.

3. Plan for a long, healthy life. With more people living well into their 90s, we need to prepare for the long haul. Consider

using a life expectancy calculator to estimate how long you might live. The "Living to 100" calculator based on data from the New England Centenarian Study, the largest study in the world of centenarians, is a great tool.[3]

How much will you continue to earn on your investments?
No one can predict the rise and fall of the stock market, but everyone can take steps to secure their income and investments. Here are a few basic ways to do that.

- Diversify your investments through a portfolio of cash, savings, CDs, stocks, bonds, ETFs, mutual funds, and real estate.
- Insure your investments through FDIC institutions that safeguard your funds in the event of bank failures.
- Consider low-risk investments through money market accounts, including CDs and U.S. Treasury securities.
- Invest with a long-term investment horizon.

While there are always risks, market swings, and volatility in investing, you can take steps to safeguard your money and watch it continue to grow. The important thing is to calculate your bottom-line returns on investments to create a lifestyle based on those numbers.

Finally, if you don't have enough money to retire today, don't despair. Get on the Super Aging fast track, and discipline yourself to pay off debt, contribute as much as you can to workplace retirement plans, IRAs, and investments, and set actionable goals for your future. As long as the needle on your readiness meter is moving, you're well on your way to retirement preparedness.

2. Insurance Audit

The second point on our Super Aging Retirement Readiness Meter is doing an in-depth audit of your insurance protection coverage. That might seem daunting, but it's a personal risk management step you don't want to avoid. Having clear knowledge of what your insurance does and does not cover will help you adequately prepare for your future and provide peace of mind.

Here are the four major expense risks that Super Agers plan for:

1. ***Protection against the cost of healthcare: Medicare and Medicare supplement insurance***

   Before the age of 65, you'll need to find healthcare coverage until you're eligible for Medicare. However, even after you're enrolled, you might need to supplement your coverage where Medicare falls short.

   That's where Medicare supplement insurance—or Medigap—comes in. This extra coverage can help with hefty deductibles or copayments and ensure you have all the support you need for the long haul. Different types of Medigap plans offer various coverage and benefits, so be sure to do your research. FreeMedSuppQuotes has a five-step guide that can help.[4]

2. ***Protection against long-term care expenses: Long-term care insurance***

   Required care that goes beyond 90 days is considered long-term care, so you'll want to make sure you have a solid, long-term care policy in place before any unforeseen injuries or health issues arise. Please don't take this option lightly. Long-term care costs can range anywhere from $3,000 to $9,000 per month or more.

3. ***Protection against loss of income: Immediate annuities***

   While you'll likely depend on Social Security, pensions, savings, and investments to cover your retirement expenses, it's wise to consider protection against loss of income. Immediate annuities are an insurance option that takes your lump-sum contribution and turns it into an ongoing source of income that spans a few years or a lifetime. Talk with your insurance agent about the types of annuities that can provide guaranteed income and offer an extra layer of protection.

4. Protection against loss from an untimely death: Life insurance
Life insurance reduces the financial impact on loved ones after your death and can even provide supplemental income during your retirement years. Your decision about life insurance policies should be based on your financial objectives and coverage for your needs. Speak with your insurance provider about the best option for your age and stage of life.

3. Budget

"Retirement is wonderful if you have two essentials—much to live on and much to live for." —Unknown

A major part of the Super Aging retirement readiness plan is creating a retirement lifestyle your budget can afford. It's easy to get this backwards and try to fit your current lifestyle into your retirement budget. However, you might need to reexamine a few things and make some changes.

Jessica and Tom (not their real names) had plans for a comfortable retirement in Las Vegas, but after the 2008–2009 economic crisis, they realized they weren't going to be able to continue living their current lifestyle for financial reasons. They ended up moving abroad and "haven't looked back since."[5]

As you envision your retirement lifestyle, keep in mind the most important things—your health and wellness, your home and community, and your financial security. You need to examine carefully anything in your current lifestyle that doesn't fit into these areas. Here's a simple exercise to help you determine what retirement lifestyle you can afford.

- Draw a circle in the middle of a sheet of paper, and write the words HEALTH, HOME, and FINANCES in the center.
- Draw lines that extend from the circle and lead to lifestyle goals such as owning your home, enjoying hobbies, traveling, and so on.
- Once you've written down all your retirement goals, check to see if all of them align with the three words in the center of the circle.
- Be sure to reevaluate any goal that doesn't promote your Super Aging HEALTH, HOME, and FINANCES lifestyle.

By the end of this exercise, you'll quickly realize which goals fit into your retirement lifestyle and which ones don't. It will help you eliminate things that don't belong and plan for the things that do.

AVOID THESE COMMON RETIREMENT MISTAKES:

- Not having a plan
- Not investing wisely
- Ignoring inflation
- Not planning for taxes
- Cashing out your savings
- Taking Social Security too early
- Not planning for healthcare costs
- Not fitting your lifestyle into your budget

4. Written Financial Plan

"Retirement planning isn't an 'old people' thing. It's a smart people thing." —Chris Hogan

Without a written financial plan, you'll likely wander through retirement like being lost in an unexplored jungle. It's a dangerous way of doing things.

Do you remember the old (or should I say, retro) Atari game *Pitfall*? The goal was to guide Pitfall Harry through the jungle without getting stuck in quicksand, crushed by rolling logs, or eaten by crocodiles. Fortunately, planning for retirement doesn't involve crocodiles, but it does often involve unexpected pitfalls. Super Agers avoid these pitfalls by developing a written plan to create financial peace of mind through each phase of retirement.

Generally, there are six phases of retirement to prepare for:

- Pre-retirement phase – the working, saving, planning years
- Retirement phase – ending employment and starting retirement years
- Honeymoon phase – traveling, trying new hobbies, and crossing things off your bucket list
- Disenchantment phase – a letdown period of wondering, "What now?"
- Reorientation phase – figuring out your retirement identity and purpose
- Routine phase – settling into your retirement lifestyle and finding contentment

Super Agers can add one more phase to retirement—the "thriving phase." It includes a healthy, well-funded lifestyle surrounded by things that matter most to you. And it starts with a solid, written plan. This is your best strategy as you prepare for retirement. The sooner you create a plan in black and white, the better. Since life expectancies continue to increase, be sure to identify both short- and long-term goals. Create plans for the next 5, 10, 20, and 30+ years.

A collaborative national study found that "financial preparedness is the gateway to retirement freedom and the antidote to retirementphobia."[6] Don't let "retirementphobia" paralyze you. Start with a written plan you can refer to often, change as needed, and develop as you go.

5. Legacy Estate Plan

"If you're going to live, leave a legacy. Make a mark on the world that can't be erased." —Maya Angelou

Do your retirement plans include up-to-date arrangements to protect your assets should you find yourself incapacitated and unable to make decisions? Preparing your legacy estate plan *now* is the only way to ensure your lifetime financial security and create a lasting legacy for the next generation.

If this isn't something you've thought of, now is the time to meet with an attorney who specializes in elder law or estate planning and is experienced in dealing with seniors' potentially complex legal and estate issues. While this might seem a bit morbid, it's actually a wake-up call to make preparations for your estate sooner rather than later.

Mildred L. Ethridge was a successful real estate broker who accumulated a lot of wealth in her lifetime. Unfortunately, she drafted her own last will and testament without consulting an attorney, which proved to be disastrous after her death. In fact, legal fights among her family members are still going on more than 25 years later.[7] Don't let her legacy become your legacy.

Here's what to include in your legacy estate plan:

- Revocable Living Trust, also known as a Family Trust, that allows you to maintain control of your estate until your passing
- Pour-Over Will that ensures your assets will automatically transfer to the established trust upon your death
- Durable Power of Attorney to determine who will make legal and financial decisions for you if you are incapacitated during your lifetime

- Health Care Directive to outline your wishes for medical care, including medication, artificial hydration and nutrition, and resuscitation
- Tax Planning to minimize the potential negative impact of estate and inheritance taxes

If you fail to put together at least a basic estate plan, the state will likely make some of the decisions for you. And if you become disabled and can't make legal decisions, the court will typically assign you a legal guardian. If you don't have an adequate estate plan in place, it's quite possible that your loved ones won't have access to or control over your assets.

Follow the needle on the *Super Aging Retirement Readiness Meter*, and be proactive in developing a written plan. View it often, keep it up-to-date, and make adjustments as life events and circumstances change.

Don't be a "Pitfall Harry" traveling through the retirement jungle worried about obstacles at every turn. Instead, take the Super Aging approach, and analyze, audit, budget, plan, and protect your assets for a thriving retirement lifestyle and lasting legacy.

Recap

Super Agers . . .

- Are empowered to gather all the information they need and diligently prepare for their future.
- Don't underestimate their retirement expenses. Instead, they take into consideration their current standard of living and are realistic about funding their retirement years.
- Create a retirement lifestyle their budget can afford by planning for the unknowns, reducing costs as they go, and planning for a long, healthy life.
- Insure themselves against the four main expense risks and work closely with their insurance advisors to choose the best policies.
- Avoid retirement pitfalls by forming a written plan to create financial peace of mind through each phase of retirement. That is the best strategy.
- Prepare their legacy estate plan *now* to ensure lifetime financial security for the next generation.
- Realize it's never too late to prepare for their future.

Super Aging Purpose of Life: Discovering Your Destiny

The way you see your life shapes your life.
How you define life determines your destiny.

Your perspective will influence how you invest your time,
spend your money, use your talents, and value your relationships.

—Pastor Rick Warren, author of *The Purpose Driven Life*

People often talk about their life's purpose as if it were something set in stone, unchangeable, and immovable. But the very definition of purpose—"to have an intention or objective toward something"—indicates an ever-changing, revolving door that leads to new goals and purposes throughout a person's life.

A young parent purposes to love and nurture their children and raise them up to be upstanding members of society. A college student purposes to earn a degree in their chosen field. A business owner or professional purposes to serve their community. But at some point, all these people will need to discover a new purpose for the new season they're in.

Aging adults often feel lost in retirement, disillusioned by the so-called golden years that once held such promise. Feeling misplaced or adrift as you age can easily be overcome by discovering a renewed passion for life.

Seeking daily purpose that both energizes you and gets you out of bed in the morning is how Super Agers move from feeling off-course to navigating their journey with confidence and joy.

They view purpose as something they *get to* discover. They are relentless in their search of a meaningful existence and constantly ask themselves motivating questions such as these:

- What is the "why" of my existence?
- What brings the most fulfillment?
- How can I contribute to the lives of others?
- At the end of my life, what do I want to be known for?

As Dr. Marc Agronin says in his book *The End of Old Age*, "Old age doesn't have to be our enemy. With purpose and the right mindset, aging is not weakness but strength. We continue to learn and grow, and while we do face adversity, we can overcome it by reinventing ourselves and gaining a sense of purpose."[1]

Super Agers have a heightened desire to reinvent themselves—to take their unique strengths and use them for a bigger, more meaningful purpose. And they don't let age stop them from investigating the multitude of exciting opportunities waiting for them.

The idea of reinventing yourself might sound intimidating and even exhausting, but it's actually both invigorating and eye-opening. Look at it this way: to reinvent something, you *breathe new life into it*. You take the structure of what's already there and make it into something fresh, new, and innovative.

Seniors are a vibrant, growing sector of our society. No longer are they thought of as past their prime. Instead, they're regarded as innovators, influencers, and trailblazers.

Imagine Your Influence

The sheer number of retirees today is astounding. Older adults make up a rapidly growing percentage of the population. The older population grew from 3 million in 1900 to 52 million in 2018.[2]

With those numbers in mind, imagine the economic, social, and political influence retirees have on the world today. Super Agers have the wisdom and experience that society needs, and retirement is the prime time for you to exert that influence. But first, you need to determine what your sphere of influence is.

SUPER AGERS ARE INNOVATORS, INFLUENCERS, AND TRAILBLAZERS

Super Aging includes living a purposeful life, one that provides personal fulfillment, satisfaction, joy, and true happiness. My hope is that by the end of this chapter, you'll not only have a renewed sense of what your purpose is during retirement but you'll have one foot out the door on the way to fulfilling it.

It starts with the people closest to you.

Your family and friends matter most on your life's journey, so your influence should start with them. Not only do they need to hear about your stories and experiences, but they also need to know the lessons you've learned along the way. Invest in those you love by sharing your hard-earned wisdom and knowledge. Encourage them, teach them, mentor them, and inspire them. They need what you have to offer.

It extends to your neighborhood and community.

Your unique gifts and abilities can and should be extended to your neighborhood and community. Participate in your local government, volunteer for a favorite charity, or start a community outreach program. You can impact your local sphere of influence for the good.

Your influence can reach more people than you might imagine.

Think of amazing people like Ruth Bader Ginsberg who influenced and inspired generations of women. Or consider Maria Shriver who is recognized for her tireless work to fight Alzheimer's disease. Then there are heroes such as Clint Eastwood who still directs award-winning movies at the age of 90 or James Earl Jones whose acting career has spanned seven decades. They are all Super Agers who have influenced more people than they ever imagined.

Super Agers are vital to the societies they live in. They've invested many years of hard work to make the world a better place. The world needs your influence!

Make Compassion a Driving Factor

Stop and think about the most inspirational people who have left an indelible mark on the world—people like Nelson Mandela, Mother Teresa, and Princess Diana. You'd probably agree that *compassion* was a driving factor of their purpose.

Viktor Frankl once said, "Being human always points, and is directed, to something, or someone, other than oneself—be it meaning to fulfill or another human being to encounter."

It's a heart of compassion that drives Super Agers to invest their time, talents, and treasures to help others. It's the retired physician serving in an inner-city community health center; the business executive imparting wisdom to a young, struggling entrepreneur; the person delivering hot dinners for Meals-on-Wheels; the volunteer building a home for Habitat for Humanity. All these people, along with countless others, are motivated by compassion-driven purpose. Caring in action not only benefits others but provides immeasurable health and wellness—both physical and emotional—to the giver.

One man, we'll call him Jim, was indecisive about when to retire from his company until he found out his younger neighbor, trained in the same field, had been without work for quite some time. Jim immediately handed in his retirement paperwork the next day and recommended his neighbor as the one to take his place. The younger man has been employed there ever since.[3]

It's stories like these—stories of compassion-driven purpose—that inspire us to retire with newfound confidence. Doubts dissipate when we know we're helping others. Complacency evaporates when you see the rewards of your investment in others. As 99-year-old actress Betty White says, "Kindness and consideration of somebody besides yourself. I think that keeps you feeling young. I really do."

Another aspect of compassion is charitable giving. Have you ever thought about the impact your charitable giving could have on others? Charitable gifts come in all shapes and sizes, from the annual donation you place in the Salvation Army red kettle to the once-in-a-lifetime contribution to establish a scholarship fund at a local college. The ways for you to give back are endless.

Here are a few more compassion-driven ideas for charitable giving:

- Support a campaign at your local hospital.
- Donate to disaster relief efforts.
- Work with at-risk youth at an after school program.
- Support a pet rescue shelter.
- Provide a well for clean drinking water to an entire village in remote Africa.

Super Agers are not only strategic in their giving, but their treasure follows their heart and passion through lifetime contributions and thoughtful legacy gifts included in their estate plans.

When rediscovering your purpose during retirement, try starting with empathy and kindness. Leave your indelible mark on the world by making compassion your driving factor. It won't be long before a whole new world of opportunity opens up to you, and people will be blessed in the process.

Keep Working (If You Want To)

Super Agers see retirement as freedom *from* work as well as freedom *to* work. By setting their own hours, determining their rates, and choosing the best fit for their new retirement lifestyle, many Super Agers choose to keep working long after their 9 to 5 jobs are over.

You might work as an Uber or Lyft driver, run an Airbnb, or operate your own food truck. There are also lots of opportunities within the "sharing economy" where individuals share products and services.

Some companies hire retirees as independent contractors for specific projects. That can be a great fit for those who still want to be involved in their career field without working full-time. One popular option for seniors is the pet-care industry. Companies such as Rover enjoy hiring seniors who enjoy animals, love staying active, and want a flexible schedule.

Explore Entrepreneurship

While some retirees are ready to kick back and relax during retirement, others are ready for an entrepreneurial adventure to pursue a passion and bring in extra income. When it comes to entrepreneurship, retirees have a great advantage—they can invest a lot of time in it. Instead of working a day job *and* a side hustle at the same time, retirees get to put however much time and energy they want into whatever interests them.

Tom started his own "keep-busy" project after retiring, not realizing his entrepreneurial exploration would turn into a lucrative business. He had heard that alpaca ranching was a good investment. He started out small and eventually built the ranch up to 133 animals. It thrived as a breeding operation and became a fulfilling endeavor.[4]

The sky is the limit when it comes to entrepreneurship. You can keep your business small and part-time or grow it into something big. The choice is yours! From selling handcrafted goods at community events to producing online courses that teach millions, your entrepreneurial dreams can reach as far and wide as you envision.

If you've been toying with the idea of exploring entrepreneurship during retirement, here are a few tips to get the ball rolling.

Do your research, and find your audience.

No matter what your passion is, do some research to find out what kind of market there is for your product or service. Look at similar businesses to see what's working (or not working). Reach out on social media to find people who are interested in what you have to offer. By doing diligent research and finding your ideal market, you'll be well on your way to starting your business on the right foot.

Find a problem, and offer a solution.

Some of the most successful businesses in the world have one thing in common: they find people's pain points and solve their problems. People are always looking for answers, remedies, and solutions to make their lives easier. Here are a few examples:

- Coaching or consulting youth, married couples, singles, or other entrepreneurs
- Ghostwriting blogs, articles, children's stories, or books
- Dog walking or pet sitting
- Cleaning and organizing homes or businesses
- Offering budgeting, finance, investing, and retirement planning

Whatever you're good at, find a way to use it to solve people's problems, and make money while you're at it. Become the go-to source in your sphere of influence, and watch your business grow organically.

Form a 90-day plan.

Many well-meaning entrepreneurs start strong but fizzle out quickly, usually due to lack of planning. When exploring entrepreneurship, form a 90-day plan that is both practical and doable. Break it down week-by-week, and set small, achievable goals. That might include setting up a simple website, gathering inventory, meeting with a marketing advisor, or gearing up for a sales event. When you *plan* for something, your chances of implementing it increase tremendously, so don't skip the planning process when you pursue your passion.

Make sure you enjoy what you do.

It's not a good idea to start a business doing something you dislike. Know your strengths, and work with them. Remember, Super Agers know what drives them. They are clear about what is most fulfilling, and they concentrate on those things. They are in touch with their personality type, their strengths, and their weaknesses.

If you've ever taken a personality test such as the Myers-Briggs, you may have been surprised at how accurate it was in assessing your preferences, your thought processes, your socialization, and your career strengths. These types of assessments can actually help you discover your purpose during retirement.

A personality test might show that you are an introvert who enjoys working alone, doing behind-the-scenes jobs, and accomplishing individual projects that bring satisfaction and meet a need. You might prefer online meetings, one-on-one consultations, and small local events. Or you might be an extrovert who is interested in teamwork, lots of social interaction, and interpersonal input. Your entrepreneurial ventures might include face-to-face encounters, group meetings, and large events. Knowing your personality type will help you pursue the right entrepreneurial passion and succeed during retirement.

If you're not interested in becoming an entrepreneur but would like to keep working during your retirement years, consider partnering with someone in your sphere of influence and contributing to their endeavor.

Travel with Purpose

Many older adults find meaning in travel as they cross off "places to see" on their bucket list and fulfill lifelong goals of seeing the world. Super Agers can find an amazing sense of adventure and purpose by experiencing all the world has to offer, meeting people in different cultures, and seeing how we're all connected.

Traveling with purpose can include visiting extended family members in places you've never been before, going on church mission trips, joining travel groups and tours, or finally making it to that dream destination. Even one dream trip after retirement can be a fulfilling way to celebrate your new season of life and complete a life-long goal.

Keep Setting Goals

Super Agers never tire of setting personal goals for their health, finances, dreams, and future. Whether it's pursuing a lifelong dream to write a book, become an artist, run a marathon, or travel around the world, Super Agers continue to set goals—big and small—in every area of life.

Jim Rohn, speaker and author of *My Philosophy for Successful Living*, writes, "Goals. There's no telling what you can do when you get inspired by them. There's no telling what you can do when you believe in them. There's no telling what will happen when you act upon them."[5] Setting goals, coming up with concrete steps to make them happen, and looking for every opportunity to implement them are the steps Super Agers take when living out their purpose.

To get started, come up with 10 big lifetime goals such as living to 100, leaving an inheritance to your children, or traveling to a dream destination. Then prioritize those goals into 10-year, 5-year, 3-year, and 1-year plans. When you see your biggest goals broken down into smaller segments of time and action, they'll be more likely to happen.

Whatever you do, don't give up. Your goals might change over time, but the key is to keep writing them down and working toward them. Bit-by-bit, you'll accomplish the things you set out to do. And you'll leave a mighty legacy in the process.

Find Your Ikigai, Your True Purpose

There's an ancient Japanese ideology called Ikigai that's been associated with a person's long life expectancy. It's all about finding joy and purpose in life.

Ikigai is what wakes you up in the morning and keeps you going day after day. It involves everything you hold dear, value most, and excel at. It takes into consideration how you can serve others in your particular strengths and gifts. The belief is that Ikigai helps you find satisfaction in what you do, so you're likely to be happier and live longer.

To find your Ikigai, start with these questions:

- What do I love doing?
- What am I good at?
- What does the world need?
- What is profitable?

Ikigai is immersing yourself in projects that reignite your passion for life and bring about a sense of purpose like you've never experienced before.

The Covid-19 Pandemic: A Reminder of the Importance of Purpose

The COVID-19 pandemic altered life for each and every person. There was a time when life seemed predictable. We had a routine. Then all of a sudden, we didn't. The pandemic caused life changes that shook up not only our daily patterns but also our psyches. You still might feel confused, fearful, and even a bit down. You might feel like you've lost your sense of purpose. So what do you do now? Where do you go from here?

Actually, the answers are entirely in your hands. And that's a good thing. If you feel you've lost your fire, there are plenty of ways to reignite it. If your life seems stuck in a rut, there are ways to get out of it. With all the time and freedom that retirement has to offer, you have total control over forging a new, purpose-driven identity. You can give your sense of self a powerful boost. Consider the following ideas.

Try Something New

Self-discovery is a great way to unearth greater purpose and appreciation for life. Is there an activity you've always wanted to try—teach a class, begin painting, try pickle ball—but didn't have the time? Is there a hobby or skill you're really good at that you've always wanted to develop further? It's very hard to feel down when your brain is actively engaged in a pursuit you love.

Socialize

Over time, social isolation and loneliness can take a toll on your health. One of the most basic human needs is feeling that you belong and are part of something bigger than yourself. Regular human connection is a good way to prevent feelings of loneliness from taking hold of your life. Who do you have strong and reliable relationships with, and how can you keep those connections going? Host a game night. Get involved at your church or synagogue. Attend an outing to the zoo. Join a program at the local library. Participate in a community event.

Spend a day shopping and going to lunch with friends. Remember, you own your schedule and how you fill it, so log some meaningful time with friends every week.

Open Your Heart

Could pet adoption be the solution to uncovering a higher purpose? We've all heard the positive research about pet ownership and the benefits of owning a dog or cat. Pets are a form of stress relief and can sometimes reduce blood pressure. They might even lower damaging stress hormones such as cortisol and boost beneficial ones such as oxytocin, (the happiness hormone).

If you're an animal lover and can take on the responsibility of a dog or a cat, it can be a fulfilling next step. Those daily walks and cuddles can certainly give you something to look forward to every day. And the new friends you meet on your walks in the neighborhood will bring you hours of enjoyment.

Connect with Nature

It's easy to feel refreshed and anew when you're surrounded by nature, so schedule some green time whenever you can. Enjoy the beauty of the outdoors by setting aside time to walk in your neighborhood, go for a bike ride, schedule a hiking trip, or volunteer at a local nature park. Wherever you live, there is a place in your community that is awe-inspiring. And if you take the time to really connect with it, you'll soon feel your stress and worry melt away.

Get Moving Every Day

Do you want to stay ahead of the aging game and maintain a healthy weight? Take time to move. Short but consistent workouts can be your secret weapon to looking and feeling younger than your years. Even if you only exercise 15 to 30 minutes a day, you can enjoy the benefits of a happier mood, a healthier heart, and a more fit body.

For even better results and more enjoyment, find a workout buddy. You're more likely to stick with your fitness program, yoga session, or

SUPER AGING PURPOSE OF LIFE

water aerobics class if you have a partner who keeps you motivated. There are plenty of fitness and exercise options, whether in an organized class or on your own.

Embrace Your New Identity

Your past career may have given you a sense of identity, but retirement life can reward you with a new one marked by freedom, creativity, and a different kind of joy. While the COVID-19 pandemic has many of us approaching life with a bit more fear, be sure to recognize your life for what it really is. It's a time of boundless opportunity to make new friends, invest in others, and enjoy a fulfilling, purposeful life. All you have to do is take the first step.

Share Your Story: Leave a Legacy

Your legacy is more than an inheritance or monetary gift. It's the essence of who you are and what you've done that you pass on to those you love. Legacy encompasses beliefs, principles, values, and accomplishments. And *everyone* leaves a legacy.

Benjamin Franklin once said, "If you would not be forgotten, as soon as you are dead and rotten, either write things worth reading, or do things worth writing."

Super Agers live each day with their legacy in mind. Whether they're content at home or traveling the world, they are mindful that what they do today matters for tomorrow. Even the humblest of people without wealth or notoriety can leave the richest of legacies to the next generation.

Author Ann Voskamp says, "When viewed from this lens of small daily actions and how they add up, creating a legacy is the most important job we can undertake."[6] Small, daily actions are *exactly* what keep Super Agers moving forward and gaining momentum. And by the end of their life, they will have built a wealth of wisdom and life experiences to pass on. It's not about fame or fortune; it's about being remembered for something special and unique.

The wonderful thing about legacy is that you can start leaving yours today. Here are few simple ideas:

- Create a family tree. Have framable prints made for extended family members.
- Write heartfelt letters to those you love, and share what you've always wanted to share.
- Pass on all your helpful life tips and bits of wisdom.
- Write down your family traditions, recipes, stories, and memories.
- Record your personal achievements, accomplishments, and successes as inspiration for the next generation.

Remember, the very definition of purpose is to have an intention or objective toward something. Your purpose might change during retirement, but it doesn't cease to exist. Discover your destiny by imagining your influence, making compassion your driving factor, keeping your goals in front of you, and leaving a legacy—starting today.

Recap

Super Agers . . .

- Have a heightened desire to reinvent themselves—to take their unique gifts and strengths and use them for a bigger, more meaningful purpose.
- Have the wisdom and experience society needs and embrace retirement as the prime time to exert that influence.
- Have a heart of compassion and allow it to drive them to invest their time, talents, and treasures to help others.
- Explore entrepreneurship as a great way to solve people's problems and make money while they're at it.
- Continue setting goals, come up with concrete steps to make them happen, and look for every opportunity to implement them.
- Live each day with their legacy in mind. By the end of their life, they have built a wealth of wisdom and life experiences to pass on to the next generation.

Super Aging Emotional Mastery: Avoiding the 7 Deadly Sins of Aging

You own your feelings. You own your thoughts. You control both.
No one has the right to any of it—to any of you without your permission.
—Carlos Wallace

There is great power in emotion—the power to love, find joy, empathize, and feel. Our emotions are wonderful, instinctive responses that help us experience life in the most meaningful ways. Because they are so powerful, they sometimes get the best of us and cause us to make rash decisions based on *feelings* rather than *facts*. We get caught up in the moment, and the intensity of our emotions overrides common-sense decisions. It's important to master our emotions so they don't master us.

Not long ago, open displays of emotion were considered unacceptable or inappropriate. There was a false belief that people who "wore their emotions on their sleeves" were unstable and less capable of making intelligent decisions. Parents from past generations taught their children to hide their emotions, stifle their feelings, and be "seen but not heard."

Fortunately, much has come to light about our intrinsic range of feelings—given to us by our Creator—that can be used as healthy responses, expressions, and interactions. Extensive research substantiates the validity of our emotions and encourages people to not only acknowledge them but also handle them with maturity and mastery.

In 1990, psychologists Peter Salovey and John Mayer introduced the first formal theory of emotional intelligence (EI). They defined EI as "the ability to monitor one's own and others' feelings and emotions, to discriminate among them, and to use this information to guide one's thinking and actions." [1]

Super Agers have learned the secret of mastering their emotions—so much so that they readily acknowledge them, process them, and utilize them in making the best decisions for both short-term and long-term success. They aren't governed by their emotions but rather are acutely aware of how they process things, act and react to certain situations, and successfully handle whatever feelings arise—realistically and intelligently.

In this chapter, we'll address the 7 deadly sins of aging in relation to our emotional intelligence and give you practical tips on how to avoid these emotional entrapments. You *can* master your emotions and reap the rewards of making clear, rational, and intelligent decisions for your life.

Deadly Sin #1: Wasting Time

"The proper function of man is to live, not to exist. I shall not waste my days in trying to prolong them. I shall use my time." —Jack London

Are you living life to the full or merely existing? That is perhaps the most important question to ask yourself as you age.

False notions of "the good years are behind me" or "I no longer have any purpose" are toxic thoughts that can derail you emotionally, mentally, and physically. These misconceptions almost always lead to a persistent lack of motivation that eventually causes you to waste days, weeks, and months. If left unchecked, these long periods of wasted time can form unwanted habits of discontent and complacency—habits that will be difficult to break.

Here are some cause-and-effect ways that wasted time can lead to a decline in your emotional well-being:

- Mindless hours of surfing the Internet, playing online games, and listening to talk radio can lead to a growing sense of discontentment, agitation, and anxiety.
- Binge watching television can become an all-consuming habit that leaves you mentally detached and apathetic.
- Waking up without a plan can lead to listless wandering from one meaningless task to another.
- Time spent worrying, fretting, and overthinking can lead to mental and emotional exhaustion.
- Living in the past with regrets and a bunch of *what ifs* can mentally drain you and make you feel worthless.

If any of these scenarios describe you, don't despair! Our Super Aging approach to managing your time will not only get you out of bed in the morning but set up your day for success.

Some people say that one of the benefits to retirement is never setting an alarm clock again. For some people, that is true. Their circadian rhythm is the only alarm clock they need. For others, maintaining a consistent daily and nightly routine is essential to keeping them energized, motivated, and able to master their emotions. The Mayo Clinic suggests, "Sleep is the foundation for a resilient life, and getting up at the same time each day (within an hour) is a healthy routine to keep."[2]

Getting your sleep schedule on track is one of the best ways to avoid wasting time during the day. Experiment with various amounts of sleep to figure out what is best for your physical, mental, and emotional health. Once you find your rhythm, you'll find that your emotions are easier to manage—all because your body clock is running smoothly.

After you've managed your sleep schedule, the next step is to make three daily goals you plan to accomplish. Try to include one big goal with two smaller, enjoyable goals. For example, if one of your goals is to write a chapter of your new book or participate in a volunteer activity, your other two goals should be less intensive such as swimming a few leisurely laps in the pool and meeting a friend for lunch.

This simple, three-goal approach is not only doable, it's motivational. Emotionally speaking, this practice will trigger plenty of feel-good emotions along with a great sense of accomplishment every day. The simplicity of this plan allows plenty of time to do the things you enjoy while pushing yourself to achieve something bigger and more purposeful.

Remember, retirement is *not* the time to shut down. It's the time to ramp up your best life. Avoid wasting time by getting yourself on a healthy sleep cycle, setting daily goals, and waking up with a more balanced, emotionally healthy mindset.

Deadly Sin #2: Sinking into Loneliness

"If you're lonely when you're alone, you're in bad company."
—Jean-Paul Sartre

Loneliness is one of the top deadly sins of aging and can lead to depression, declining mental health, and a host of adverse physical reactions. While it's normal to go through short seasons of loneliness, if you're not careful, those short bouts can turn into days and months of isolation. This has a negative effect on your emotional intelligence as it slowly chips away at your sense of well-being and self-assurance.

According to the teaching on emotional intelligence and the elderly, "The terms 'isolation' and 'loneliness' are often used interchangeably, but they refer to two distinct concepts. Isolation refers to separation from social or familial contact, community involvement, or access to services. Loneliness, by contrast, can be understood as an individual's personal, subjective sense of lacking these things to the extent that they are wanted or needed. It is therefore possible to be isolated without being lonely, and to be lonely without being isolated."[3]

Instead of sinking into loneliness, your best plan of action is to get out and about. A brisk walk in the sunshine and in nature can do wonders for the mind, body, and soul. Attending a class at the local university, signing up for a fitness program, or doing something special for a neighbor can lift the cloud of loneliness and help you feel connected.

If loneliness is a familiar companion, determine to make that phone call, send that email, deliver that invitation, or go to that event. Remember the childhood mantra, "To make a friend, you have to be a friend." Don't let feelings of insecurity or inadequacy stop you from reaching out. Be brave, and engage with people around you. Your emotional health needs regular interaction.

WAYS TO OVERCOME FEELINGS OF LONELINESS

- Volunteer at a children's hospital, nursing home, soup kitchen, or animal shelter.

- Join a local meet-up based on your interests such as food, travel, sports, or entrepreneurship.

- Get plenty of fresh air, sunshine, and outdoor exercise.

- Join an online multi-player game site to play Rummy, Chess, or Uno with friends.

- Open up to trusted friends and family members about your feelings of loss or isolation.

Sometimes we battle feelings of loneliness even when we're surrounded by family and people we care about or are engaged in social activities. In most cases, that's due to invisible barriers we've put up, guarding ourselves against getting too close to someone, or letting our true selves show. It's a defense that protects us from getting hurt or facing rejection.

As a Super Ager, you don't have to worry about rejection. You are confident in who you are and what you believe. You happily interact with others on a deeper level without anything to hide. All pretense is gone!

If you're wondering how to let your guard down and *really* connect with someone, start by allowing your own vulnerabilities to show. When people see that you're open, honest, and authentic, they'll begin to relax around you, which leads to deeper interactions. You'll soon find those invisible barriers coming down and your feelings of loneliness vanishing.

Here are a few conversation ideas to consider when trying to connect with others on a deeper level:

- "Even though I've never been through that, I can certainly empathize with your situation."
- "No matter what, we are on this journey together."
- "I'm always here to listen and encourage."
- "I feel like a better person after spending time with you."
- "You enrich my life."

Don't embrace loneliness as a companion. Isolation is never a good friend. Instead, strive for authentic engagement with people, and schedule regular time to hang out with them. Your relationships will become like emotional wells that fill up when you spend quality time together. Keep in mind that relationships take effort. Real connection doesn't happen overnight. However, through determination and commitment, you'll develop those deep, lasting relationships that keep you from sinking into isolation and prevent prolonged seasons of loneliness.

Deadly Sin #3: Losing Yourself through Loss

"You will lose someone you can't live without, and your heart will be badly broken. . . . And you come through. It's like having a broken leg

that never heals perfectly—that still hurts when the weather gets cold,
but you learn to dance with the limp." —Anne Lamott

Loss and grief are inevitable parts of the human existence. Of course, we wish they weren't, but they are. As we age, the loss of siblings, classmates, and spouses makes death even more of a reality. Through these losses, we are changed—sometimes for the better but often for the worse, especially when our identity is wrapped up in the person who passed. When they die, we sometimes allow our identity to die with them.

Mastering your emotions now plays a vital role in helping you deal with grief and maintain who you are. Acknowledging the full extent of your pain, allowing yourself time to mourn, and then determining to move forward one small step at a time are ways to prevent loss of purpose and identity. As Lamott said, "You learn to dance with the limp."

Super Agers guard against loss being the demise of their hopes, dreams, and future goals. They allow grief to come, and then they work through it. They always keep the big picture of life in mind. Though the grief process is painful, they view it as a strengthening rather than a weakening experience. In the end, they come away from loss a little bit stronger than before.

Dorree Lynn, a 77-year-old psychologist in Charleston, South Carolina, says this about loss: "Not everyone can overcome it, but those who are resilient enough to navigate this dance with mortality well can find wisdom and everyday joy made sweeter by the depletion of time."[4] What a perspective! Dorree's emotional mastery has allowed her to grieve her personal losses, stay resilient, and find joy in daily life.

Instead of losing yourself through loss, use your experience as a learning process to master your emotions for your good and the good of others. Don't hesitate to reach out for help and talk with a counselor or therapist. Let others help you through the stages of grief so you can regain your bearings and live purposefully once again.

Finally, try to find opportunities to express your loss in a positive way—by journaling, joining a grief-share group, recording your memories, or creating a memory box to share with your kids and grandkids. Loss is both painful and real, but it's not the end of your story. Master the emotional tide of grief by allowing the waves to come but not overwhelm you in the process.

Deadly Sin #4: Allowing Negativity to Rule

"When we pity ourselves all we see is ourselves. When we have problems, all we see are our problems. . . . We don't see the good things in our lives." —Ann Marie Aguilar

All of us are wired differently. Some people have a natural propensity to see things through the proverbial rose-colored glasses, while others view things with skepticism, looking for the negative in most situations. Interestingly, there's actually something called "negativity bias." Dr. Talib Kafaji in his book *The Psychology behind Wellness and Illness* wrote, "Our negative bias means that we spend too much time ruminating over the minor frustrations we experience in our daily lives, such as bad traffic, or a disagreement with a loved one, while ignoring the many chances we have to experience wonder, awe, blessings, and gratitude throughout the day."[5]

This explanation holds an emotional key for those who want to be positive thinkers but struggle with the constant battle of negativity. The key is *gratitude*. Positive thoughts written down or spoken aloud during bouts of negativity can become a lifelong habit that turns even the most negative person into someone who sees the brighter side of things. Not all Super Agers are naturally positive people, but they are able to recognize negative thought patterns and take positive actions to flip their mindset. Through deliberate practice and faithful persistence, we *can* master chronic negativity.

Here are a few practical things you can do to flip the switch on negativity:

1. Get to the root of your emotions. Sometimes the surface issue that's causing the negative reaction isn't what is *really* bothering you. Get to the root cause so you can deal with the situation appropriately instead of negatively.

2. Keep a gratitude journal, and write a list of things you are grateful for each day. When tempted to wallow in negativity, read through your journal as a reminder of the good things in your life.

3. Ask yourself if there's any lesson you can learn in the moment— something good you can take with you—no matter how frustrating the situation is.

4. Spend time with positive people. You are more likely to come away from a positive person feeling uplifted and ready to spread positivity yourself.

Often, negativity is a disguise for something deeper. Anger, regret, defeat, self-pity, or a lack of self-worth can be emotional strongholds that prevent a person from having a bright, positive outlook. When you recognize these deeper issues, you can deal with them through self-realization, spiritual awakening, and emotional counseling. Over time, you will replace your negative reactions with positive, thoughtful responses.

If you've let negativity rule your emotions, start today to introduce more gratitude into your life. It's one step toward emotional mastery that will make a tremendous difference in your attitude and frame of mind.

Deadly Sin #5: Neglecting Your Brain Health

"Whenever we feel stressed out, that's a signal that our brains are pumping out stress hormones. If sustained over months and years, those hormones can ruin our health and make us a nervous wreck."
—*Daniel Goleman*

As I've mentioned before, emotions are powerful. They help us celebrate life to the fullest and help us cope with difficult trials. But there are destructive emotions that are so toxic that they affect the functions of our brains and can even destroy our brain health if we don't monitor them carefully.

These destructive emotions have a variety of names—tension, strain, worry, anxiety, agitation, nervousness, affliction. But they all fall under one overarching umbrella— *stress*.

Persistent stress over many months or years can cause major brain issues such as memory loss, attention deficit, sleep issues, panic attacks, and overreactions to everyday situations. The brutal effects of constant stress on the brain cannot be overstated.

One older adult (we'll call him John) describes his stress this way: "It's a feeling that someone is gripping the back of my neck tightly. And I'm so tense that I can't even turn around to see who it is—even if I wanted to."[6]

Fortunately, we now know more about stress than ever before and can make informed decisions regarding our emotional health. According to the Anxiety and Depression Association of America, there's "a direct link between stress trajectories and mortality in an aging population, men who experience persistently moderate or high levels of stressful life events over a number of years have a 50 percent higher mortality rate." [7]

With this kind of information, we are better equipped to stop stress in its tracks and step onto a healthier path of stress management and stress reduction. Through practical exercises such as yoga, meditation and prayer, breathing techniques, fresh air, and sunshine, as well as time spent on relaxing hobbies, we can reduce our stress levels and release some feel-good hormones.

For some, mastering chronic stress might mean a psychological evaluation and medical treatment. That is nothing to be ashamed of. Take your emotional health seriously. Seek the help you need, and get stress under control. Don't allow this emotional tyrant to destroy your brain health.

Deadly Sin # 6: Surrendering to Depression

"I have depression. But I prefer to say, 'I battle' depression instead of 'I suffer' with it. Because depression hits, but I hit back. Battle on."[8]
—*Anonymous*

Of all the emotional battles we face, I think it's safe to say that depression is one of the most common. There's a very real and persistent struggle for many of us to find the balance between short seasons of "the blues" and prolonged seasons of depression that could indicate a serious problem.

Some of the telltale signs of depression are trouble with concentration, changes in appetite, disrupted sleep patterns, fatigue, low sex drive, loss of interest in activities you once enjoyed, feelings of helplessness or hopelessness, unexplained digestive issues, and persistent feelings of sadness.

While intermittent periods of these emotional disruptions are normal, prolonged symptoms usually indicate a more serious concern. Depression isn't something you can just snap out of. Many factors contribute to depression, including brain chemistry imbalances, hormone fluctuations, seasonal changes, and trauma. So how can we manage depressive feelings without surrendering to them?

Start with a full physical examination. Work with your doctor to find out what is causing your depression. There's no use trying to master depressive emotions if there's an underlying medical cause. Rule out any physical anomalies before dealing with the emotional side.

Once you've spoken with your medical professional, invest in a trusted counselor or psychologist to help walk you through the various emotional and psychological issues tied to depression. Discuss all the possible factors, including loss of self-worth, past trauma, overwhelming circumstances, chronic worry, relationship problems, or unmet needs.

Super Agers are the first to admit when they are depressed. They take action before it becomes an insurmountable problem. They aren't ashamed to admit when they need help, and they're persistent in finding the right people to guide them. Don't surrender to depression. Fight the battle with an arsenal of support that will get you on the path to victory and emotional mastery.

Deadly Sin #7: Giving In to Fear

"The oldest and strongest emotion of mankind is fear, and the oldest and strongest kind of fear is fear of the unknown." —H. P. Lovecraft

The path to retirement is lined with nervous excitement and healthy fear of the life ahead. We make plans and embrace lifestyle changes to prepare for the Golden Years.

However, many aging adults view this road as dark, dangerous, and full of twists and turns that might lead to a dead end. They get stuck in fear and allow it to create a barricade between the life they want to live and their perceived notions of what *might* happen.

Common fears about aging such as loss of independence, declining health, financial burdens, and even the fear of death can become overwhelming fears that wreak emotional havoc. These feelings of helplessness can leave a person paralyzed and unable to carry out their purpose.

Well-known singer Barbara Streisand admits that stage fright kept her from performing for 27 years. Her debilitating battle with fear finally came to an end when she began listening to motivational tapes and following the mantra "let go and let God." [9]

Super Agers aren't numb to fear, but they are proactive when conquering it. Their mindset is that fear is a real emotion that requires deliberate action. Like a mountain climber starting at the base of a massive fourteener, it starts with one solid step upward. Mountains of fear become manageable by taking one faithful step after another.

Here is a step-by-step approach to mastering fear:

1. Name your fears. Identify exactly what you're afraid of. This exercise might bring about a bit of anxiety, but it's important to give your fears a specific name so you can address them directly.

2. Consider worst-case and best-case scenarios. What is the worst that will happen if your fears come true? What is the best that will happen if they don't? One study by the Department of Psychology at the University of Pennsylvania found after monitoring people's fears over a period of time that 91% of those fears never occured.[10] That type of study has been proved over and over, indicating that many of our perceived fears will never come to pass.

3. Plan for success. Conquer each and every fear by planning your life in spite of them. Are you worried about your financial well-being? Meet with a financial advisor to make solid plans for your future. Are you fearful about declining health? Meet regularly with your doctor, health coach, and nutritionist to plan the best habits for optimal wellness. Turn your fears into plans. That's the best way to reach the summit of success.

4. Surround yourself with support. Fears tend to grow when we isolate ourselves and allow too much introspection. Get involved with outgoing, goal-oriented people who will encourage and inspire you. Consider finding a support group for seniors in your area. Chances are that you'll find other aging adults who are battling their own fears and need your encouragement and camaraderie.

A healthy amount of fear is expected as we enter the Golden Years, but don't let it become a barrier to a happy, content life. Instead, turn your fears into actions, and master this emotional obstacle to joy and peace.

Improve your emotional intelligence by resisting these 7 deadly sins of aging. This could be the most important aspect to outsmarting the effects of aging and living like you are decades younger.

Recap

Super Agers . . .

- Don't waste time. Instead, they implement a three-goal approach to do things they enjoy while pushing themselves to achieve things that are bigger and more purposeful.
- Guard against loneliness by interacting with others on a deeper level and striving for authentic engagement.
- Navigate loss by letting others help them through the stages of grief. They look for opportunities to express their loss in a positive way.
- Are able to recognize negative thought patterns and take positive actions to flip their mindset.
- Master chronic stress and take their brain health seriously.
- Are the first to admit when they are depressed and take action before it becomes an insurmountable problem.
- Are proactive in conquering their fears by naming them, planning for them, and surrounding themselves with support.
- Master their emotions and improve their emotional intelligence for a happy, content life.

Super Aging Home & Community:
Discovering the Best Place to Super Age

*"We cannot live only for ourselves. A thousand fibers
connect us with our fellow men."*

—Herman Melville

We all have an attachment to *place*, a corner of the world where we belong, connect, and identify best. Like the characters in our favorite sitcoms *Friends* or *Cheers*, we all want to fit in, have people we can count on, and find a place where "everybody knows your name."

Whether you've lived in the same place your whole life or moved around more times than you can count, discovering the best place to Super Age takes thoughtful consideration and deliberate planning. It doesn't matter the size, location, or style of your home as long as it's the place that best supports your Super Aging lifestyle.

In this chapter, we'll look at the *keys to finding a great place to Super Age*, but first, let's start with three questions you need to ask yourself.

1. What matters most to me?
2. What do I want to shape my life around?
3. Who are the people I should factor in to my decision?

Answering these questions upfront will keep you centered on your values, goals, and tribe as you decide where to Super Age. After all, you could live in the most luxurious place on earth and still miss out on the things that are most valuable to you. On the other hand, you could live in the humblest of places and be surrounded by everything that matters most.

Here's an exercise to help you answer the three questions.

On a sheet of paper, draw a line down the middle to form two columns. At the top of the left-hand column, write "Most Important." At the top of the right-hand column, write "Places to Super Age."

In the left-hand column, answer the questions listed below. Be as detailed as you can. In the right-hand column, list some possible places to retire—even your dream destinations. When you're finished, cross out any places that don't align with your answers on the left.

Questions:

- What kind of home will bring you the most joy and contentment (e.g., single family home, condominium, apartment, one-story living, big yard, recreation room?)
- What people do you want to "do life" with (e.g., kids, grandkids, friends, church members, etc.)?
- What climate will be most conducive to your health and lifestyle (e.g., mountains, beaches, countryside, etc.)?
- If you are married, what things are important to your spouse? Do you both share the same vision for retirement?
- What type of community will give you the most support and opportunity to Super Age?

What did you discover through this exercise? Were you surprised at some of your answers?

Keep this list handy as you explore all your home and community options.

Now let's move on to the *keys to finding a great place to Super Age.*

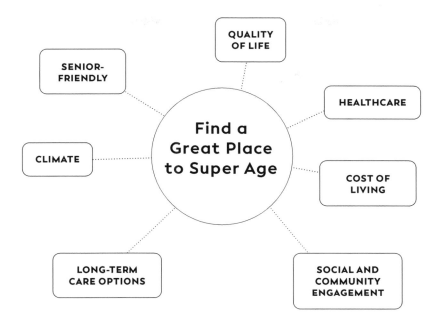

1. Quality of Life

Perhaps you've heard of the Blue Zones—regions of the world where people are the most healthy and happy, and live the longest. According to Dan Buettner, Blue Zones founder, "The secret to longevity, as I see it, has less to do with diet, or even exercise, and more to do with the environment in which a person lives: social and physical."[1]

Buettner's research concluded that a person's quality of life is based on something he calls the Power 9,[2] the habits listed below that are found in the Blue Zones, the most thriving communities in the world.

- Move naturally by doing things that are enjoyable to you such as gardening or hiking.
- Know your purpose by tapping into what motivates you to get out of bed each day.
- Downshift by taking regular breaks to destress and relax.

- Follow the 80% rule by eating small portions until you are 80% full.
- Incorporate the "plant slant" by making beans, legumes, and vegetables the majority of your diet.
- Enjoy "wine at five" by having one or two glasses of wine in the evening.
- Find your "right tribe," and spend time with friends and family that supports a healthy lifestyle.
- Belong by joining a faith-based community.
- Keep family and loved ones close by making them a priority.

Seriously consider your quality of life by investigating the environment where you want to live. Where will you find the lowest crime rates, accessibility to services, activities for healthy living, and feasibility for family to visit? Location matters, but your quality of life matters more.

With these things in mind, here are the top five Blue Zone locations in the world: Icaria, Greece; Sardinia, Italy; Okinawa, Japan; Nicoya, Costa Rica; and Loma Linda, California.

If you've always dreamed of moving to your favorite vacation spot, keep in mind that just because you liked someplace on vacation doesn't mean it will be a great place to live. It's always wise to test your Super Aging location before setting down roots.

Depending on what phase of retirement you're in (especially in the beginning stages), you have room to experiment a little and alter your plans, if necessary. Remember to stick to your most important list, and don't get derailed. I've witnessed friends who have followed their kids across the country, got sick of relocating after a while, and finally decided to retire where *they* wanted to. Your list of what matters most is key to keeping you focused.

2. Healthcare

Finding a great place to Super Age must include affordable healthcare options. Look for communities with excellent hospitals and modern medical facilities. Search for the most qualified doctors, nurses, and specialists. You may also benefit by seeking the advice of a geriatrician, a doctor who specializes in treating older adults.

While your Super Ager lifestyle includes a healthy diet, regular exercise, and activities to strengthen your mind, it's also wise to be prepared for the inevitable—aging slowdown. Routine blood work and screening tests for vision, hearing loss, memory, mobility, and balance should become your top priority, along with your yearly exams and dental appointments. Research has shown that many diseases common to seniors, including high blood pressure, high cholesterol, and depression, may be prevented or delayed with proper screening.

Your health and wellness are a top priority as you age, so don't overlook accessibility to great medical care—hospitals, outpatient specialty care, rehabilitation services, and doctors—as key factors in deciding the best place to retire.

3. Cost of Living

Numbers don't lie. Your budget is a *huge* determining factor for your Super Aging home and community. Whether you're staying put or making a big move, you need to become *very* acquainted with your finances.

There's a relatable verse in the Bible that says, "For which of you, desiring to build a tower, does not first sit down and count the cost, whether he has enough to complete it?" (Luke 14:28 ESV)

What a great reminder to sit down and count the cost. We'll be taking an in-depth look at the financial aspect of the Super Aging Framework in another chapter. But for now, understand that it's important to assess the cost of living, taxation, and overall affordability of the place you ultimately choose to retire.

For Super Agers looking to extend their working careers, find part-time employment, or start a business, discovering a place with a vibrant economy, easy travel access, and business growth opportunities is also an important financial consideration.

Not only should your budget include plans for the next few months, but it should also include extended plans for the next three years, five years, ten years, and more. Keep in mind that long-term care options are typically not covered by Medicare or secondary insurance, so you will need personal savings or long-term care insurance to cover the costs. Medicaid and other government programs usually cover many long-term care costs once you meet certain income and asset requirements.

Aging in Place

Many Super Agers plan to age in place—a concept that's been reframed in recent years. If you want to remain in your home for the long haul, you'll need to equip your surroundings with everything you need to be safe and efficient.

Smart home technologies such as Alexa or Echo systems, home security alarms, cameras, and even robotic assistance are modern technologies that can set you up for success. In 2019, *Time* magazine introduced Stevie, a robot integrated into the Knollwood Military Retirement Community in Washington, DC, as a "socially assistive robot . . . designed to help users by engaging with them socially as well as physically."[3] With constant new advancements, it won't be long before artificial intelligence (AI) becomes a go-to source of assistance for Super Agers.

Along with these modern technologies are systems that provide predictive monitoring, including smart sensors that keep track of a person's movements, collect data, and notify loved ones if any issues arise. "By integrating the smart home data with vitals captured from wellness sensors, a trend (slower movement a few days before a stroke, for instance) could be spotted and anticipated before a serious accident occurs."[4]

The decision to age in place includes carefully evaluating your home for possible health hazards. That doesn't mean you resign yourself to accidents; in fact, it's quite the opposite. Modifying your home *before* accidents happen is being proactive, proficient, and prepared. A few home modifications to consider are walk-in baths, shower safety bars, ramps, stair lifts, and wider doorways.

One program called Safe at Home "provides no-cost preventive home modifications to people with mobility issues and other disabilities to improve accessibility, reduce falls, increase independence, and facilitate aging-in place."[5]

Besides safety and efficiency, you'll also need to consider basic household upkeep such as regular home maintenance, lawn care, snow removal, and more. When you step back and reevaluate your current location, try to view it long term. Count the cost when deciding whether aging in place is the right decision for you.

> **SUPER AGERS UNDERSTAND THAT "HOME" IS A SACRED PLACE. IT'S NOT WHERE YOU ARE BUT WHO YOU ARE.**
> Choosing a place to live comes by answering these questions:
> * What matters most to me?
> * What do I want to shape my life around?
> * Who are the people that factor into my decision?

Smart Sizing

In her 70's, Bette Presley decided she'd had enough of big-house living. She joined the Tiny House Movement and now enjoys the freedom of having "fewer possessions, greater mobility, and more time and money to spend."[6]

Tiny-house living isn't for everyone, and fortunately, there's an alternative called "smart sizing." It's a relatively new concept that is all about creating a lifestyle of simplicity that fits your physical space.

A few smart-sizing factors to consider are what living spaces are most important to you (family room, office, backyard, etc.). Will your belongings fit nicely into the new space? How will you maintain the home? And can you afford to smart size, or do you need to downsize?

For the Adventurer at Heart

Super Agers who are looking to add a bit of adventure to life have plenty of out-of-the-box options. They can be as inexpensive or pricey as your budget allows.

Options such as RVs and motor homes have never been more popular. They range from $10,000 to $500,000 and cost anywhere from $500 to $1,000 per month to camp at a typical RV park, depending on the location. Approximately one million Americans (many retired) live full-time in their RVs.

Sailing, cruising, and house-boating are also popular retirement alternatives. An average houseboat costs $50,000 to $1 million or more, and the average cost of living in a houseboat community is $5,000 to $10,000 per year.

Alister Punton and Shannon Lee recently co-founded Storylines, a residential community that continuously travels the world in a 627-suite ocean liner that can host 1,000+ residents and 450+ staff. You can purchase a suite for $300,000 to $8 million with a monthly, all-inclusive fee of $2,300+ per person. The ship's perks include 20 unique dining venues, onboard activities, a garden farm, a microbrewery, wellness spas and fitness centers, and much more. It could be an ideal choice for Super Agers who are looking to live out their passion for five-star exploration on the high seas.

If you are thinking about retiring overseas, you aren't alone. In 2019, more than 430,000 retired US workers lived overseas and received their Social Security benefits (www.ssa.org). But keep in mind that the *keys to finding a great place to Super Age* are still important considerations if you decide to retire outside the United States. Be sure to research residency and visa requirements, online banking, Social Security payment requirements, medical insurance, local laws, and how best to prepare for emergencies.

A couple of great online resources you will want to check out are International Living and the Expat Info Desk. A master course on retiring overseas called Retirement Reimagined! was created by Edd and Cynthia Staton who are retiring abroad experts. Also, be sure to visit the U.S. State Department's website for current travel information, restrictions, and advisories.

Whether you choose to age in place, smart size, downsize, travel across America in an RV, or live overseas, do your research. NewRetirement has a plethora of checklists, quizzes, and tips to help you make the best decisions.[7] They are planning steps you don't want to skip.

4. Social and Community Engagement

Newspaper columnist Barbara Bernard (a woman in her 90s) is a great example of someone who is socially engaged in her community. She's described as "a woman who rarely acts her age . . . swims at the YMCA each weekday morning . . . and then attends Mass at her parish church. She plays bridge at least twice a week and hosts a high-stakes (I'm talking wagers in terms of dimes here) card party at her home each Monday afternoon."[8]

Being a Super Ager like Barbara is all about social and community engagement. When searching for the best places to Super Age, look for libraries, social events, entertainment centers, volunteer opportunities, religious and civic groups, and continued learning and educational services. Organized educational, cultural, and fitness activities reduce social isolation and improve physical and mental health and the overall quality of life.

If recreational activities such as fitness classes, aquatic programs, racquet sports, and group running or walking give you enjoyment, make sure you make them a priority in your planning. A local YMCA, Jewish Community Center, or Area Agency on Aging is a great place to find available resources in your community.

Remember, life is not a solo journey. It's best enjoyed with people you love and connect with. Make social and community engagement a priority when you're looking for your best place to Super Age.

5. Long-Term Care Options

You may have heard the idiom "turn on a dime." It refers to things that can take a sharp turn without a moment's notice. And there's one thing we understand about life on this planet—life's circumstances can change in an instant. As business coach Jeffrey Shaw says, "After these 'turn on a dime' moments, it's all about choice. You are now empowered to make a different choice. Your mindset has been forever altered and each and every action step you take towards your objectives is your choice."[9]

No matter what your plans are for Super Aging, make flexibility your friend. Plan for the long term, and avoid depending on friends and family to provide for you. Each generation is dealing with their own financial responsibilities, so it's up to Super Agers to plan for their future. Keep in mind that long-term care options are typically not covered by Medicare or secondary insurance. According to the Administration on Aging, someone who turns 65 today has a nearly 70% chance of requiring some form of long-term care and services during their lifetime.[10]

With that in mind, let's look at several long-term choices to consider.

Home Care

Home care falls in line with aging in place but includes in-home services for cleaning, cooking, bathing, and transportation. This is an attractive option for most Super Agers as they remain independent for as long as possible and get to stay in the home they love. It's a good idea to interview several reputable home care agencies, discuss a plan of care, and ask about their supervision process and caregiver training.

Make sure home aides are insured and bonded and that there is access to quality physician care.

It's important to note that the home-care option might require more help from family and friends as time goes on, so take that into consideration as you move forward.

Assisted Living

With US Baby Boomers—77 million strong—heading into their Golden Years, assisted living is growing at a record pace. Today there are more than 30,000 assisted living facilities in the United States alone, with approximately a million beds. With these statistics, you can see the inevitable strain the elder care system will eventually experience.

Assisted living is for aging adults who are still somewhat independent but need assistance with the activities of daily living, including meal preparation, medication administration, bathing, dressing, and transportation. Assisted living communities usually consist of small-apartment complexes with full-time staff who are available to residents. Contrary to common belief, assisted living facilities aren't the same as nursing homes. Residents still maintain as much independence as possible but have round-the-clock staff to assist them when needed. Genworth has a handy online tool to help you calculate the cost of community care in your state.[11]

For military veterans and their spouses, the VA Aid & Attendance Pension may provide an option to pay for or defray the costs of assisted living, nursing care, and certain home care for individuals who qualify and meet certain income requirements. Veterans and their spouses can complete VA Form 21-2680 and mail it to the Pension Management Center in their home state or apply in person at their local Veterans Administration office.

Memory Care

In 2020, the Alzheimer's Association cited an estimated 5.8 million Americans above the age of 65 who are living with Alzheimer's disease.

At the current rate, this number is expected to increase to 13.8 million people by 2050. [12]

Memory care is similar to assisted living, but it is reserved for older adults who are dealing with memory impairment that is likely to progress. Memory care facilities include memory-enhancing activities and therapies, specially trained staff and caregivers, behavioral management and care coordination, assistance with the activities of daily living, and enhanced security measures such as safety monitors and tracking systems. If you're concerned about cognitive issues, don't hesitate to meet with your doctor to receive a proper diagnosis and begin to plan accordingly.

Nursing Facilities

In the event you no longer feel safe or capable of living alone, a nursing home or skilled nursing facility might be the optimal choice for you. These facilities that are home to nearly 4 million Americans offer 24-hour nursing care and include the following services:

- Room and board
- Rehabilitation therapies
- Nursing care
- Physician care
- Occupational, recreational, and speech therapy

Talk openly with your loved ones about nursing home options, and be sure to look for things such as quality, cleanliness, friendliness of staff, and comprehensive services. For more information on nursing facilities, check out *U.S. News & World Report*, which annually rates about 16,000 nursing homes nationwide. [13]

Retirement Communities

Retirement communities (typically for people ages 55+) come in various types and sizes and are excellent options to keep in mind. They include independent living and Continuing Care Retirement Communities (CCRCs), which are also known as life plan communities. Not only do they provide a thriving community of support, but they help Super Agers maintain their independence.

The Villages, known as "Florida's friendliest hometown," is one of America's largest and best known retirement communities with more than 125,000 residents spanning three counties. It offers more than 3,000 clubs and activities, 42 executive golf courses, and much more.[14]

Unlike aging in place, retirement communities offer amenities such as life-enrichment programs, peer support, concert and cultural programs, travel and learning opportunities, and expansive wellness and fitness options. Super Agers everywhere are discovering outstanding retirement communities that fit their lifestyle needs. Think of it as an all-inclusive destination that might end up being the very best option for you.

SPOTLIGHT ON SHELL POINT RETIREMENT COMMUNITY

Shell Point Retirement Community offers an unparalleled resort lifestyle in a beautiful waterfront setting along the Caloosahatchee River in Fort Myers, Florida, just minutes from the Gulf of Mexico and the islands of Sanibel and Captiva. A nationally recognized award-winning Continuing Care Retirement Community (CCRC), Shell Point provides an array of residential choices in five neighborhoods, many with waterfront or golf course views. Shell Point includes a marina with deep water access, five restaurants, a 1,000 seat church auditorium, an 18-hole championship golf course, numerous swimming pools, fitness centers, and miles of scenic walking and biking trails on a 700-acre campus surrounded by nature preserves and waterways. Continuing education and lifelong learning are provided through the Academy at Shell Point, and a world-class arts center offers dozens of artisan clubs and groups, a 400-seat performing arts hall for concerts and live performances, and studios for a variety of artistic pursuits, including pottery, painting, literary arts, dance, music, and more. Residents enjoy this active, carefree lifestyle in a beautiful setting that also provides state-of-the-art healthcare and the assurance of life care, with independent living, assisted living, skilled nursing, and memory care, all located on one campus.

6. Climate

Most people don't stop to consider the year-round climate when looking for places to retire. However, things like air quality, humidity, and altitude can pose significant problems for people with sensitivities. Go back to the list of things that are most conducive to your health and lifestyle.

Some of the states with the best weather year-round are Hawaii, California, Arizona, Texas, and Florida. These states feature lots of outdoor activities and fitness options, as well as warm temperatures and plenty of sunshine. States with the best air quality are Alaska, Oregon, Washington, Ohio, and Maine.

When it comes to climate, choose what fits your needs and preferences, and be sure to do your research.

7. Senior-Friendly

You've probably realized by now that being a Super Ager is all about thriving. And when it comes to choosing your retirement destination, make sure it's a senior-friendly place.
Here are some specific things to look for:

- Accessible and affordable housing
- Safe neighborhoods with low crime rates
- Sufficient medical doctors and specialists
- Libraries
- Senior transportation
- Programs that promote intergenerational interaction
- Walkability
- Senior centers
- Supportive services such as Meals-on-Wheels, adult day care, and visiting nurses associations that promote an independent lifestyle

Nearly 100 million Americans live in one of the 507 communities nationwide that participate in the AARP Network of Age Friendly States and Communities. Age-friendly communities encourage inclusion and perspectives from residents of all ages. In addition, the AARP Public Policy Institute created a "livability index" that measures quality of life and livability within a community. To check out the livability in a community, visit www.livabilityindex.aarp.org.

If a place doesn't offer senior-friendly services, it might not be the right place to retire. Choose a place that helps you live your best active, meaningful, and purposeful life.

Remember, the best place to retire is the one that supports your Super Aging lifestyle, is within your budget, and helps you not only survive but thrive. We know it's not an easy decision, and there are many things you can't predict. But by answering the three big questions at the beginning of this chapter, you are definitely headed in the right direction.

> *"The power of community to create health is far greater than any physician, clinic or hospital."*
> Mark, Hyman, M.D. Founder, The UltraWellness Center

Recap

Super Agers . . .

- Find great places to retire depending on what matters most to them, what they want to shape their life around, and what people factor into their decision.
- Understand that location matters, but quality of life matters more.
- Realize their health and wellness is a top priority and know that accessibility to great medical care facilities is *key* in deciding the best place to Super Age.
- Factor in the cost of living whether they choose to age in place, relocate, smart size, or downsize.
- Plan for long-term care to avoid depending on friends and family to provide for them.
- Consider adding a little adventure to retirement, including living in an RV or a houseboat, cruising the high seas, or living overseas.
- Consider the year-round climate of the place they're interested in and do diligent research on things such as air quality, humidity, and altitude.
- Know that Super Aging is all about thriving. They make sure their retirement destination is senior-friendly with resources and programs that promote an active lifestyle.

Super Aging Perks:
Amazing Things No One
Told You about Aging

Wrinkles will only go where the smiles have been.

—Jimmy Buffet

Well, you've done it. You are entering the fabulous third act of your life. The stage lights are on you, so take a bow, receive the applause, and let yourself bask in the limelight a little longer. You deserve it!

Believe it or not, there are some wonderfully unique things about aging—perks that no one has told you about. They are often forgotten in the midst of all the changes, but they are, indeed, the undeniable perks of aging and aging well.

As author Tricia Cusden says, "We should go into a period of renaissance rather than retirement, and feel younger as we explore new adventures, later in life."[1]

Renaissance, as you know, indicates a period of rebirth, revival, and innovation. This perspective aligns perfectly with Super Aging. After all, your retirement years should be more about revival than survival. They should always lead to new opportunities for personal growth and transformation.

So take center stage as we open the curtain to the amazing things no one has ever told you about aging.

Happier with a Better Sense of Well-Being

In your 20s, happiness was likely a fleeting occurrence based on your weekly paycheck and your date for the weekend. As you moved into your 30s and 40s, you found happiness in the ups and downs of raising your kids, finding contentment in marriage, and establishing your career. But as you grew older, you finally had time to take a breath—a deep breath that says, "Job well done."

Happiness is by far the biggest perk of aging. A sense of well-being can settle into your soul as you exhale youthful pursuits and inhale joy and contentment. Gratitude overcomes worry. Peace replaces stress. And your days look brighter than ever before.

Studies by Northwestern University and the University at Buffalo found that as people age, they are more likely to "look at the bright side of things" and "experience increases in happiness over time."[2] That's because older adults typically learn to see the best in people, trust on a deeper level, and overlook small offenses that used to bother them. Feelings of satisfaction, contentment, and security follow Super Agers throughout their lives in these four areas of well-being:

1. Physical – practicing good health habits in order to have the energy to do the things you love and enjoy
2. Social – nurturing relationships that are most important to you
3. Community – enjoying your home, your environment, and your community by staying connected and involved
4. Purpose – being energized by what motivates you and continuing to fulfill your life goals

Despite the changes and challenges that come with transitioning into retirement, happiness and well-being are in the forefront. Don't let gloom-and-doom naysayers have the last word. Super Agers truly are some of the happiest people around—and *you* are one of them!

Nicer as You Age

In the 1993 comedy *Grumpy Old Men* starring Walter Matthau and Jack Lemmon, these older adults can't help but bicker, complain, and criticize. Fortunately, this fictional movie is exactly that—fictional.

The truth is that Super Agers get nicer as they age. They let small things go, allow minor irritations to roll off their backs, and look for ways to be helpful. Instead of becoming crotchety old people, they become more friendly, outgoing, and positive.

Because they are emotionally stable, Super Agers find it easy to be compatible and agreeable. They have personalities that light up a room. Ready to listen, share stories, give advice, and help where they can, retirees have an aura of friendliness about them that people are attracted to.

Even the crankiest people can learn to be nicer in old age. By managing negative thoughts, recognizing the things they want to change, learning to control reactive behaviors, and focusing on kindness, even the most stubborn can change their ways.

Remember, becoming a grumpy old man (or woman) isn't the norm. Becoming your kindest, friendliest self is.

Enjoy More Self Confidence

Goodbye, insecurity. Self-confidence has taken your place. The great news about getting older is that previous concerns about self-image, work performance, and what other people think about you diminish greatly.

Super Agers reject stereotypes such as *ageism,* which discriminates against people based on their age, in favor of positive viewpoints that help them hold their heads high and live with mature confidence.

By paying close attention to the following areas, Super Agers embrace confidence as a major perk to aging:

1. Outward appearance – Looking good during retirement means less about fashion trends and cosmetic treatments and more about getting ready to seize the day. It's being attractive through approachability, friendliness, and a sense of purpose.

2. Physical strength – Meeting physical goals such as walking 30 minutes every day or training for a 5K gives most people an unbelievable amount of confidence. The feelings of accomplishment you'll experience through physical health will radiate from every pore and give you plenty of energy for the years ahead.

3. Continued learning – Educating yourself throughout retirement is a major confidence booster and includes many free and paid opportunities. College lectures, community classes, online courses, and self-study are ways you can improve your confidence and continue learning no matter what your age.

4. Secure connections – Staying connected with the right people encourages self-confidence by motivating you to invest in amazing people and exciting opportunities. Great friends provide overall confidence in who you are and what you can do.

For those who struggle with confidence, Harvard Men's Health Watch says, "The best way to regain confidence is to remind yourself of your capabilities, address the obstacles that keep you from feeling confident, and work around those obstacles."[3]

As a Super Ager, your capabilities are endless. The obstacles in your life are more than conquerable, and *now* is the time to be more confident than you've ever been.

You Will Be Less Stressed and More at Rest

A life without stress is . . . well, impossible.

As we talked about in an earlier chapter, chronic stress can create chaos in all your body's systems—mental, emotional, and physical. But what if the occasional encounter of heightened stress levels could be used to your advantage? An exciting experience such as a big move, a rare travel opportunity, or a new business venture naturally gives rise to higher stress levels. However, Super Agers are able to channel those stressors into motivation, pushing them to reach the end goal successfully.

Super Agers utilize stress to help them be more efficient, driven, and centered on getting things done. In the end, they are far less stressed about petty, insignificant things and are quick to find solutions, consider all their options, pivot if needed, and go another direction entirely. It's these mature coping skills that enable Super Agers to handle stress with a sense of calm resilience. Because they are able to process life events logically with a nothing-new-under-the-sun perspective, their outlook is generally more relaxed and carefree.

Along with a persistent ability to cope with stress, Super Agers maintain a healthy perception of time. They don't get lost in regrets of the past or focus on the mistakes they made. Rather, they look forward to the years ahead and resolve to finish well.

10 SIMPLE HABITS TO RELIEVE STRESS

1. Get enough quality sleep each night.
2. Exercise regularly by finding physical activities you enjoy.
3. Spend time in the great outdoors getting plenty of fresh air and sunshine.
4. Practice meditation, yoga, mindfulness, and other deep-breathing techniques.
5. Reduce your caffeine intake.
6. Consider getting a pet for companionship.
7. Spend time with those you love most.
8. Laugh often.
9. Listen to music, paint, or craft with your hands.
10. Journal your thoughts, feelings, and emotions.

Being less stressed and more at rest is an amazing perk of aging that no one has told you about. There's no more fretting over small details or trying to control everyone and everything around you. There's no more losing sleep over insignificant things, and no more constant cycles of worry that consume your mind.

For Super Agers, chronic stress is a thing of the past, and contentment is their new reality. The normal amounts of stress that life serves is met with calm, clear, and concise patterns of making it work in their favor.

Better Sex and Deeper Intimacy

Dim the lights, and turn on a Lionel Richie soundtrack. The truth about Super Aging sex and intimacy is about to knock your socks off. If you've believed the myth that older people don't engage in or aren't able to have sex, I'm afraid you've been highly mistaken. Many older adults experience better sex and deeper intimacy than when they were in their 30s or 40s.

Here are a few key areas where sexuality improves with age.

Body image – Super Agers have learned to accept their bodies and have grown comfortable in their own skins. Insecurity about physical flaws is replaced with a sense of freedom they've never before experienced. They see themselves in the best light, faults and all, and decide to enjoy sexual intimacy without the hindrance of insecurity or self-condemnation.

Performance – While sexual arousal might take a bit longer as you age, the need to perform for your spouse is replaced with intentional and meaningful intimacy. It might include other means of sexual pleasure besides intercourse such as kissing, caressing, massaging, and exploring. As Natalie Wilton, a social worker in the field of elder care, says, "Sexuality in late life may involve reframing goals and preferences."[4]

116

Super Aging couples have matured beyond sexual pressure and performance and have settled into mutual enjoyment. That relieves many issues in the bedroom and is certainly an added perk to aging.

Communication – Super Agers aren't afraid to discuss their sexual needs openly and honestly. In fact, they are rather intentional about discussing their desires and listening to their spouse's preferences. These open lines of communication are not only refreshing, but they often lead to better sexual fulfillment as more outspoken desires are met.

Unity – Just as bicycles built for two work in tandem, sex as you age works in tandem as well. Deeper intimacy is cultivated through the amount of time Super Agers spend together, and their relaxed approach to sexuality leads to a more fulfilling experience. Closeness, companionship, and comfortability unify couples as they age, which cultivates an even greater sense of satisfaction in the bedroom.

One suggestion for older couples who struggle with sexuality is to role play or follow a guide book on how to spark intimate conversation and promote physical exploration. Sometimes just talking about sex leads to arousal and the initiation of sexual connection. If problems persist, don't hesitate to reach out to your doctor for advice. After all, these are the years to fully enjoy your significant other and experience better sex and deeper intimacy.

More Empathy

There is a difference between sympathy and empathy. Sympathy occurs when a person has been through a similar circumstance and understands to a certain degree what someone else is going through. Empathy, on the other hand, is being able to say, "I haven't experienced what you have, but I'm here to listen and help however I can."

Empathy settles disputes, connects people of differing beliefs, crosses lines of separation, and unites the world. I cannot overstate the need for more empathy. Psychology experts reviewed data over a period of many years that involved 740 adults. They examined how empathy changed over time from the ages of 13 to 72. Not surprisingly, they found that people tend to become more empathic as they get older, sympathizing with others when bad things happen and trying to take others' perspectives when they don't agree on things.[5]

Being more empathetic is a major characteristic of Super Agers and leads to stronger relationships, meaningful interactions (even with strangers), and a greater motivation for volunteer or mission work. The myth that people grow reclusive or stand-offish with age is debunked as older adults engage empathetically with the world around them—a much needed attribute in our world today.

Plenty of Wisdom to Share

There's a proverb in the Bible that says it's much better to have wisdom than gold or silver. In essence, it says that wisdom is more valuable than any tangible item. Why? Wisdom deepens a person's understanding, not only about practical things such as work, marriage, family, and wealth, but also about deeper things such as love, loss, and life after death. Wisdom gives insight into what makes the world go 'round and leads to thoughtful, intelligent discussions that get people thinking.

Dilip Jeste, M.D., author of *Wiser: The Scientific Roots of Wisdom, Compassion, and What Makes Us Good,* states, "Wisdom may be defined as a complex human trait with several specific components: social decision making, emotional regulation, prosocial behaviors, self-reflection, acceptance of uncertainty, decisiveness and spirituality."[6]

Super Agers have plenty of wisdom to share. They use their life experiences, personal hardships, captivating stories, and unique testimonies to make a lasting impact on those around them. The more insight they share, the more people view them as go-to sources of wisdom and understanding.

Don't underestimate the wisdom you have to offer. Your life matters. Your experiences can help others who are going through something similar. Look for ways to impart your wisdom through one-on-one mentorship or at that next family gathering. Wisdom is more precious than gold—and you have plenty to share!

More Emotionally Stable and Less Impulsive

The tallest roller coaster in the world measures more than 450 feet high and travels at speeds over 120 miles per hour. As most roller coasters do, the cars roll slowly out of the station, climb the first tower with intensity, and then drop straight down into a stomach-lurching plunge.

Sound familiar?

Our emotions are known to mimic the unpredictability of a roller-coaster ride, changing without warning, accelerating at full speed, and dropping underneath us. For many people, their emotions take them on a wild ride of ups and downs that leaves them disillusioned and discouraged.

Fortunately, Super Agers are much more emotionally stable and less impulsive as they age. Their once unpredictable onslaught of feelings has settled into rational thoughts, ideas, and behaviors. Instead of experiencing the sharp twists and turns of unmanaged emotions, Super Agers have learned the art of stability.

They are less likely to make rash decisions based on pressure from others. They avoid impulsive purchases. They are able to spot family drama a mile away and keep themselves from being drawn in. They keep their anger in check.

As psychology professor Laura Cartensen says, "If people become more even-keeled as they age, older societies could be wiser and kinder societies."[7]

What an incredible perk to be able to handle life through an even-keeled approach that betters society! Super Agers definitely know how to step off the ride of unpredictability and live emotionally stable, less impulsive lives—for the good of everyone around them.

A Stronger Spiritual Perspective

The last act of a person's life almost always brings about more reflection of the meaning of life and what happens after death. Spiritual perspectives that were once fluid and malleable become stable and centered as people realize their days are numbered.

Aging adults are more apt to investigate religion, faith, and spiritual practices as they contemplate eternal ideas. For some, this can bring on a sense of fear or unease. For Super Agers, there is little fear but instead a strong spiritual perspective and dependence on God.

The calm realization that life is "but a breath," as mentioned in the Bible, becomes more of a reality and often leads Super Agers into a deeper understanding of eternity. King Solomon wrote in Ecclesiastes, "God has made everything beautiful for its own time. He has planted eternity in the human heart."[8]

Of all the amazing perks of aging, having a solid spiritual perspective is the most reassuring. Being able to look beyond the here and now and embrace the next life with peace and assurance is both necessary and unavoidable. If you've been questioning your spirituality, consider meeting with a spiritual mentor to discuss it. Ask questions, start your own personal faith journey, and read all you can. Talk to friends and family you respect, and ask God for a clear perspective about life, faith, and the afterlife. You don't have to walk in spiritual darkness. You can know for sure what happens next.

Ultimately, your retirement years should be about renewal and rebirth. This "Renaissance" period should usher you into a time of deeper satisfaction and sense of well-being for today and all your tomorrows. People may not shout from the rooftops the amazing perks of aging, but they exist nonetheless.

Enjoy these years. Embrace every wonderful opportunity you can. Live every moment as if it were your last, and be a shining example of the abundant life you have as a Super Ager. People are watching, and it's up to you to paint the beautiful picture of what a Super Ager looks like. And oh, what a masterpiece it is!

Recap

Super Agers . . .

- Look for new opportunities for personal growth and transformation.
- Enjoy happiness as the biggest perk of aging and include five key areas of well-being—physical, financial, social, community, and purpose.
- Get nicer as they age and become more compatible, agreeable, and friendly.
- Embrace confidence as a major perk to aging with a positive approach to outward appearance, physical strength, continued learning, and secure connections.
- Utilize stress to help them be more efficient, driven, and centered on getting things done, which leads to less stress and more rest.
- Have matured beyond sexual pressure and performance and have settled into mutual enjoyment, leading to better sex and deeper intimacy.
- Are empathetic, which leads to stronger relationships, meaningful interactions, and a greater motivation for volunteer or mission work.
- Have plenty of wisdom to share and use their life experiences to make a lasting impact on those around them.
- Are more emotionally stable and less impulsive since they have learned the art of stability.
- Have a solid spiritual perspective and are able to look beyond the here and now and embrace the next life with peace and assurance.

Super Aging in America:
How Super Agers Respond
to Growing Trends

Trends, like horses, are easier to ride in the direction they are going.

—John Naisbitt, author of *Megatrends, Ten New Directions
Transforming Our Lives*

The definition of a *trend* is "a general direction in which something is developing or changing." Many trends come and go without much change or lasting impact. But some trends, especially the ones we're seeing today, are having a direct impact on aging adults. That's why we've created this chapter to point out growing trends in America and provide Super Aging responses to the changes happening in our country.

To get started, here are a few statistics worth noting:

- By about the year 2034, the number of people age 65 and older will exceed the number of people 18 and younger for the first time in US history.
- When the youngest Baby Boomers (those born in 1964) reach retirement age, one in every five Americans will be a senior citizen.
- By 2060, there will be 2.5 working-age adults for every retirement-age person. In 2020, that ratio was about 3.5.
- The median age in the United States is expected to be 43 by 2060. (It was 38 in 2020 and 29 in 1960.)

No matter how many different ways you look at them, the statistics are startling. They show how the Baby Boomer generation—people born between 1946 and 1964—continues to shape our economy, institutions, and culture.

The 2020 census estimates that about 73 million Baby Boomers are living in the United States today. As we move further into the 21st century, we've identified eight trends that reveal how this group is carving out a new way of aging in America.[1]

Trend #1: Changing Public Policies

This large, active voting population of older citizens has the power to make their voices heard at the ballot box. They also have a vested interest in public policies such as Social Security and Medicare.

However, with so many Americans at retirement age, both Social Security and Medicare have a fundamental math problem—they are paying out more than they are taking in. With nearly 60 percent of current retirees claiming that Social Security is a significant source of their retirement income, an upcoming shortfall is looming.

According to projections, Social Security will not have enough funds to pay out benefits and expenditures by the mid to late 2030s. The problem has far-reaching implications for every American since a 2019 Federal Reserve survey found that one-fourth of all workers have saved nothing for retirement. Many of those who did have savings at the time of the survey had to dip into them to stay afloat during the COVID-19 pandemic.[2]

The Super Agers' Response: As active, well-informed voters, Super Agers are the first to uphold better policies and practices. They write to their senators, join public forums and senior advocacy programs, and lend support for the rights of aging Americans everywhere.

Older voters demand the attention of policymakers and respond by leading the way, making their voices heard, and taking positive action for future generations.

Trend #2: Continued Participation in the Workforce

A person's 65th birthday is no longer retirement day for many Americans. In fact, the over-65 age group is the fastest-growing segment of the U.S. labor force, according to the U.S. Bureau of Labor Statistics (BLS).[3]

The BLS projects that 13 million people age 65 and older will still be working by 2024. While the total number of workers is expected to grow by 5% over the next decade, the number of workers ages 65 to 74 will increase by 55%. In the 75 and older group, the total will jump an astonishing 86%.[4]

While some seniors keep working strictly out of financial necessity, others do it for the sense of purpose and meaning it gives to their lives. Phased retirements will be a growing trend as companies offer their senior workers the option to reduce their working hours as they transition to retirement.

These programs are a win-win. They enable the older, experienced, and productive employee to work fewer hours while still engaging in their profession and earning an income. At the same time, the employer saves on payroll and benefits by having a senior-level employee who can train younger workers.

Many older workers are also switching to self-employment and remote work as a way to maintain some form of income and stay active in their careers. We believe that savvy employers will hire older workers more and more as independent contractors, freelancers and so-called gig workers. New technologies will continue to develop and allow people of all ages and experience to work remotely even more than they are.

The Super Ager's Response: With a lifetime of work experience under their belts, Super Agers know the value they bring to the workplace. They get to decide how many hours are conducive to their Super Aging lifestyle and can continue working as long as it is beneficial to their future goals.

With a sense of purpose and working on their terms, Super Agers move forward in their strengths, offering strong leadership skills to younger employees and becoming a source of dependability for savvy employers. With confidence, Super Agers respond to continued participation in the workforce as an option that ultimately leads to a more personally fulfilling and financially secure retirement.

Trend #3: Increased Focus on Health Span (Not Just Lifespan)

Super Agers have impacted much of America's culture throughout the decades, and Baby Boomers are changing what it means to be elderly. They are more health-conscious and engaged in their medical care than previous generations.

Another way to look at it is that the Baby Boomer generation is not just interested in having a long lifespan; they are interested in living better and longer. Life expectancy (currently 77.8 years for Americans) is an estimate of the years the average person is expected to live. In contrast, healthy life expectancy (or health span) estimates the years someone might live in a healthy state. According to the World Health Organization (WHO), the average American's healthy life expectancy is 68.5 years.[5]

Baby Boomers have launched an anti-aging revolution, and we should see increased marketing efforts toward that age group in health and wellness products and services in the coming years. Those products will most likely include everything from new and improved home exercise equipment to cosmetic surgery, clothing, vitamin supplements, and new smart technologies—all to make life better and easier.

Researchers are also looking closely at the biology of aging versus the biology of age-related diseases in a revolutionary study called geroscience. The research examines basic biological mechanisms such as genetics, molecular structure, and cellular mechanisms that may lead to chronic conditions in older people. It has enabled scientists and others interested in health and aging to consider interventions that could lead to improved longevity by keeping people healthier longer.[6]

The Super Ager's Response: Seniors are putting their money where their health is. Even though a majority of American marketing dollars target young people, Baby Boomers continue to set buying trends by purchasing organic, natural foods and fresh ingredients, as well as quality supplements and other products that promote health and vitality.

Super Agers continue to focus on the whole person and pay close attention to their physical, emotional, and spiritual health. They embrace nutrition, exercise, relationships with others, and new technologies that help them live a better life. With this proactive response to longevity, Super Agers are paving the way for longer life spans coupled with excellent health spans.

Trend #4: Looming Long-Term Care Crisis

According to the report *Aging in Place: A State Survey of Livability Policies and Practices*, about 90% of people over age 65 want to remain living in their homes as long as possible. Of those respondents, 80% said they believed their current home is where they will live out their lives.[7]

However, since many older people require some assistance to remain safely in their homes long-term, aging in place will require some major shifts in our society. Let's look at three components of this looming healthcare crisis.

1. Many people enter old age single (either widowed or divorced), which means they can't count on a spouse to care for them. In addition, their adult children are likely living and working in another city or state and raising their own families.
2. There is a shortage of home healthcare workers. Many positions go unfilled due to low pay and stressful working conditions.
3. The rising cost of long-term care—either in the home or at an assisted-living facility—is out of reach for many families. Data

from a 2020 Genworth Cost of Care Study shows the following national median annual costs:

- Assisted living facility – $51,600 per year
- Home services with "hands-off" tasks such as cooking, cleaning, and running errands – $53,768 per year
- Home health services with "hands-on" personal assistance such as bathing, dressing, and eating – $54,912 per year
- Semi-private room in a skilled nursing facility – $93,075 per year
- Private room in a skilled nursing facility – $105,850 per year[8]

Some states are taking action to help their adult citizens pay for long-term care (LTC). For example, Hawaii's Kapuna Caregivers Program provides subsidies for adult daycare, home aides, transportation, and meal services. Washington became the first state to approve publicly funded LTC, providing benefits up to $36,000 to help families pay for in-home care, assisted living, or a nursing home. Fortunately, other states are likely to follow suit.

Long-term care insurance and annuities, along with life insurance that provides long-term care riders, are options that will likely grow in popularity in the coming years. However, both public and private sectors will need to develop more widely accepted and affordable options for the growing long-term care dilemma.

The Super Ager's Response: Fully aware of the looming long-term care crisis, Super Agers are advocating for more affordable senior housing options and publicly funded long-term care provisions. They are working with financial professionals to diligently plan for their future, not relying on family members but investing in long-term care solutions that will provide for them the rest of their lives.

With a no-fear approach, Super Agers respond to the long- term care crisis by consciously planning for the future, maximizing their independence and securing the housing options their budget will support.

Trend #5: New Technology Aimed at Seniors

The increased demand for quality affordable elder care—especially care that allows seniors to remain at home—is leading to increased innovation. Most of these technologies were already underway before the COVID-19 pandemic, but they got on the fast track during the shutdowns when many seniors were more isolated than ever.

Telehealth, or virtual meetings with healthcare providers, makes it more convenient and less expensive for people to get treatment for many health conditions. Through advances in remote patient monitoring technology, seniors can connect with their healthcare providers for a wide range of services. They include tracking vital signs with remote devices, talking with a nurse or counselor through a web portal, and receiving care from a doctor via a video call.

Robotics and artificial intelligence (AI) are offering new ways for seniors to get help at home. Medical robots, which are already in use in nursing homes in Japan and some parts of Europe, perform small personal tasks such as retrieving food and water or giving medication reminders. Some robots provide social engagement through games, while others use hydraulics to help provide mobility and physical support. Robots are also showing promise in memory care. The Robotics website, for example, shows pet-style robots that help comfort dementia patients who experience Sundowner's Syndrome, a condition where someone becomes more confused, agitated, and anxious as late afternoon transitions into evening.[9]

We will continue to see more advanced home-tech devices such as improved fall monitors, security cameras, and virtual assistants that help people age safely at home. Progress will continue to be made in implantable health devices, 3D printing of organs, smartphone apps, and a host of genetic and life science advances meant to increase longevity and health span.

The Super Ager's Response: Embracing the newest technology in support of longevity is at the forefront of every Super Ager's health goals. Super Agers are first in line to discuss innovative healthcare with their providers and take advantage of Telehealth, smart home technologies, wearable technology for personal health and exercise, robotics, artificial intelligence, and medical monitors. There's no doubt that Super Agers will lead the way in implementing advanced in-home devices to make their retirement years safe, comfortable, and relevant.

Trend #6: Senior-Friendly States and Communities

The 65-and-older population varies greatly by state, although a movement to make states senior-friendly will continue in the foreseeable future. In 2019, 51% of people over the age of 65 lived in nine states, with the highest percentage of seniors residing in Maine (21%), Florida (21%), and West Virginia (20%). States that continue to offer low-cost living, plentiful senior housing options, a lower tax environment, and great healthcare options will continue to lure new senior residents.[10]

Growing advocacy for healthy aging will call for greater investments in our social infrastructure to help seniors age in place while maintaining a high quality of life and feeling more engaged in their communities. Some advocates' wish-list items include the following:

- Improved access to public transportation
- Public parks, buildings, and connected walkways that offer easy access and safe walkability
- Affordable housing with modifications to help seniors age in place, including handrails, better lighting, and wider hallways and walkways to accommodate wheelchairs and walkers
- Opportunities for volunteer and paid work
- Community programs designed to bring younger and older people together

A movement in other countries known as age-friendly communities is now becoming popular in the United States. An age-friendly community supports and enables residents to age actively by adapting its services and structures to be inclusive of and accessible to people of all ages and abilities. As of March 2021, 511 communities in the United States were participating in the AARP Network of Age-Friendly States and Communities.[11]

The Super Ager's Response: Super Agers become their own advocates in their communities and promote expanded social opportunities for aging adults. They research the best age-friendly states and are willing to move if it means better quality for the long term.

Through active participation in their city governments and the dedicated support of local developments in infrastructure, Super Agers work tirelessly to create and maintain senior- friendly environments for their communities. They will continue to move to places in the United States and overseas that offer a great quality of life, outstanding healthcare options, a low cost of living, and low taxes.

Trend #7: Inequalities of Aging

Over the course of the COVID-19 pandemic, we witnessed many racial and economic inequities in our nation. These disparities are causing some disturbing trends in our older population. To put it simply, wealthy, highly educated people tend to live longer. Research shows that helping our older population live well may depend less on medical progress and more on policies that reduce socioeconomic differences in healthcare access.

Evidence is also building that an older person's health may reflect the conditions they have experienced throughout their lives. Researchers are only beginning to understand how childhood disadvantages influence health and mortality in old age. This ongoing research will help policymakers identify ways to make early investments in nutrition and education that can improve health at any age.

Geography also plays a part in health inequalities. Older people living in rural locations tend to have poorer health than people in urban areas, and suburbanites tend to fare worse than their urban counterparts. Reasons for these differences may include fewer options for healthcare and longer travel times to access adequate healthcare facilities.

Researchers are also finding that socioeconomic status may make some older adults more at risk for dementia. A complicated set of factors can influence someone's chance of developing dementia, including early home life, education, cognitive stimulation, social networks, and genetics. Understanding the causes of dementia and early intervention could help address disparities in the risk of the disease by ensuring equal access to the resources that contribute to healthy brain function.

There is no one-size-fits-all prescription for healthy aging. Experts believe that big data analytics and genetic research over the coming years could be the answer to preventing these inequalities and offering more personalized medical care in the coming years. We also may see breakthroughs in the use of biomarker tests in predicting dementia and Alzheimer's disease.

The Super Ager's Response: All forms of inequality are unacceptable to Super Agers, and the current trend is motivating them to identify ways to change healthcare and economic disparities among the elderly. Super Agers are continually on the lookout for political, social, and economic ways to improve the lives of all seniors and make a difference now and for the future.

Trend #8: Changing Attitudes about Aging

There are a couple of classic marketing phrases that go something like this: "This is not your grandfather's Buick" and "This is not your mother's kind of vacation."

These phrases are intended to show that a particular product or service is not outdated or old-fashioned and should be noticed as new and improved. These ads proliferate despite the fact that today's grandpa is more vibrant and active than his grandfather was at the same age, and today's grandmother is more adventurous than ever.

Sadly, stereotyping older adults is still a problem. An AARP survey found that about three in five older workers have either seen or experienced age discrimination in the workplace. More than 75% of these older workers view age discrimination as a problem in finding a new job. Another AARP report found that more than half of older workers reported being pushed out of long-time jobs prematurely.[12]

These surveys were published in 2019, and unfortunately, the pandemic only made things worse for ageism in the workplace. During a recent webinar sponsored by the Longevity Project, Dr. Louise Aronson, author of the 2020 Pulitzer Prize finalist book *Elderhood*, said the pandemic spread some misconceptions about what it looks like to be a senior in America today. He explained that even though only about 3% of older people live in skilled nursing homes, the many news references to frail old people during the pandemic reinforced false stereotypes of what it means to grow older. This aging expert offered hope that we can apply some of the work young people are doing to combat other "isms" in America and counter ageism as we move further into the 21st century.[13]

Although a society's negative perspective on aging is something that is hard to measure and even harder to change, some communities are working on it. In 2019, San Francisco became one of the first US cities to launch a public awareness program designed to disrupt negative stereotypes of older adults and connect seniors with support services. Nearly a third of San Francisco residents will be age 60 or older by 2030. According to a news release about the project, ageism in San Francisco is affecting all ages, the workplace, community engagement, and public policies.[14]

Many seniors feel the challenge of living in two separate worlds. In one world, they are staying productive, healthy, working members of society much longer than previous generations. And yet they also live in another world where their opportunities are limited or cut short because of age bias.

The Super Ager's Response: Stopping ageism is an uphill battle, and the Baby Boomer generation is doing its best to do just that. The sheer number of active, older Americans in advocacy groups such as AARP (38 million members) demonstrates that Super Agers continue to wield a great deal of influence in this country. They intend to prove that seniors are valuable members of the workforce and society and that America needs their knowledge, skills, and presence in order to make influential changes for good.

The graying of America cannot be stopped and should, in fact, be embraced as a new season of wisdom, strength, and dynamic change for America's seniors. Not only is this a time for Super Agers to exercise much-needed influence for the good of this country, but it's time for them to help steer things in favor of aging adults in every sector of society. The bottom line is that aging in America is both positive and significant, and deserves to be held in the highest regard. Be a Super Ager who is aware of the growing trends and actively participates in the changes needed to empower every senior in America.

Recap

Super Agers . . .

- Are the first to uphold better policies and practices. They are diligent in lending support for the rights of all aging Americans.
- Advocate for more affordable senior housing options and publicly funded, long-term care provisions, maximizing their independence and securing the housing options their budget will support.
- Are continually on the lookout for political, social, and economic ways to improve the lives of all seniors and make a difference now and in the future.
- Continue to wield a great deal of influence in this country, and America needs their knowledge, skills, and presence to make meaningful changes for good.

CHAPTER 11

Super Aging Champion: Taking the Next Step

Life will only change when you become more committed to your dreams than you are to your comfort zone.

—Billy Cox

It's never too late to be a Super Ager. Anyone—no matter when, where, or how they start—can map out the rest of their life based on the Super Aging Framework.

The key is to *start*.

Mark Twain once said, "The secret of getting ahead is getting started." And you are already ahead simply because you picked up this book! You are taking your future seriously. You *know* there is a better way to age, and you are determined to outsmart the effects of conventional aging and live as though you were decades younger.

Now that you've discovered a better way to live during retirement, it's time to develop your personalized plan. First, pinpoint your location as if your future were an atlas on the wall. Now ask yourself where you'd like to go next. It doesn't matter where your starting point is. You are where you are for a reason, and the only way to go is forward.

Not only is it important to visualize your journey, but it's crucial to put it in writing. Tangibly seeing the plan in front of you will help clarify your destination and point you in the direction you need to go.

For starters, use the Super Aging Framework, and list specific actions you want to focus on over the next 90 days.

1. Mindset: Moving from Fear to Empowerment
2. Health & Wellness Lifestyle: Achieving Better Health for a Better You

3. Relationships: Staying Connected during Retirement
4. Retirement Readiness: Preparing Your Finances for Retirement
5. Purpose of Life: Discovering Your Destiny
6. Emotional Mastery: Avoiding the 7 Deadly Sins of Aging
7. Home & Community: Discovering the Best Place to Super Age
8. Perks: Amazing Things No One Told You about Aging
9. America: How Super Agers Respond to Growing Trends
10. Champion: Take the Next Step

Think of it as a 90-day challenge—three months to improve your life and gain momentum toward your end goal. Keep a monthly calendar in plain view, and mark each day you take action. That might sound simplistic, but it's a powerful way to see progress and stay inspired.

However, don't do this 90-day challenge alone. As you write out your plan, put together your Super Aging team, including your spouse, healthcare providers, friends, fitness instructors, mentors, and spiritual guides. List all the people who are going to help you, encourage you, and challenge you to become a successful Super Ager. Contact them. Tell them about your new and improved Super Aging lifestyle. And most of all, express how important they are on your Super Aging journey.

You've likely heard the African proverb about raising a child—"It takes a village." The wisdom in it is that a child needs to be raised in a healthy, positive, secure, connected, and well-rounded environment in order to be successful in life. And the people surrounding that child (their village) makes this happen.

In the same sense, it takes a village for Super Agers to be well-rounded, happy, and successful in their mindset, health and wellness, community, finances, relationships, emotional mastery, and purpose. Your personal team of people—your tribe—is key to your success. Don't travel on this journey alone. Invite your support team to come along for the ride. You'll be amazed at how empowering it is to have trusted people to support you at every crossroad along the way.

SUPER AGING CHAMPION

90-DAY CHALLENGE

Clearly describe what Super Aging will look like for you in one year. (Use specific, measurable objectives with numbers and dates.)

_____

_____

_____

_____

What can you do in the next 90 days to ensure success to your one-year goals and objectives?

_____

_____

_____

_____

_____

MINDSET: What 3 fears do I need to conquer in the next 90 days?

1. _____

2. _____

3. _____

HEALTH & WELLNESS: What 3 health habits can I implement to improve my health?

1. _____

2. _____

3. _____

RELATIONSHIPS: Who are 3 family members and/or friends I will improve my relationship with in the next 90 days?

1. _____
2. _____
3. _____

FINANCES: What are 3 goals that will secure my financial security?

1. _____
2. _____
3. _____

PURPOSE: What 3 ways will I (re)discover my purpose in the next 90 days?

1. _____
2. _____
3. _____

EMOTIONAL MASTERY: What 3 negative emotions will I improve starting today?

1. _____
2. _____
3. _____

HOME & COMMUNITY: What matters most to my quality of life as I Super Age?

1. _____
2. _____
3. _____

Finally, and perhaps most importantly, discover lasting happiness in retirement and life by focusing on your SOUL.

Seek meaning in life and in everything you do.

Outlive yourself by keeping your legacy front and center.

Understand that your health is priority #1, and create lasting habits for optimal wellness.

Love life's little moments, and live fully in the present.

So much of what we do and how we do it is a reflection of what's going on inside. By focusing on the deeper "why" of how you're living life, you'll discover areas you need to change in order to successfully achieve the Super Aging lifestyle.

In the words of 98-year-old author Babette Hughes, "Start having success in whatever you decide to do. Success is the jet fuel to keep going."

Your jet fuel is your SOUL actions and beliefs. These deeply motivated actions—developing a new health habit and keeping it, being intentional in life's small moments, and cultivating relationships that truly matter—will propel you forward as a Super Ager. Each time you take a SOUL action and reap the benefits that follow, you'll be inspired to take the next empowered step.

And here's the big question: Where do you want to go from here? Remember, you get to choose the route, how long it will take you to get there, and the speed you'll travel. But ultimately, you must forge your own path.

Jo Ann Jenkins, author of *Disrupt Aging*, writes, "Shortly after my fiftieth birthday, and with newfound determination, I decided to really own my age and follow my own path."[1] Jenkins, along with countless other Super Agers, are *owning* their age and stage in life. They are looking in the mirror and saying to themselves, "You've got this—now get going!"

With one bold step of determination, Super Agers break free from the conventional stereotypes of aging and live empowered, successful, and deeply satisfying lives. No longer are they stuck in poor health, inactivity, lack of purpose, or dead-end relationships. Their future is mapped out with the end goal in sight—a fulfilled life of significance.

The famous Route 66, also known as the Mother Road, is a 2,400-mile highway that spans eight states from Illinois to California. Along this well-worn stretch of highway, travelers encounter ghost towns that hint of the good ol' days, roadside diners that serve endless cups of coffee and all-American cuisine, and quirky attractions such as the world's largest rocking chair. While travelers never know who or what they might encounter, it's the sense of freedom and adventure that entices them to make the renowned journey.

Super Agers pave their own Route 66. From point A to point B with memorable stops along the way, they breeze through places that don't interest them and linger in communities where they find the greatest connection, opportunity, and impact.

They *prepare* for the journey ahead.

So where are you on the journey? Look around, and decide what needs to change in order for you to live your best life now. What is the most immediate part of the Super Aging Framework that will move you forward to a life of freedom and empowerment? Take actionable steps on that issue *this week*. Then choose one more pillar to address, and tackle it the following week. Soon you'll look back and realize you got serious about your future and did something amazing.

What are you going to accomplish from this day forward? Throughout this book you have seen dozens of time-tested, proven ideas for how you can live with purpose and make retirement your best years. This isn't a one-size-fits-all plan but rather a framework you can use to create a Super Ager lifestyle that rises above the cultural norms and expectations of aging and allows you to live with extraordinary confidence and determination.

Nothing is standing in your way! You have everything you need to succeed as a Super Ager. Take the next step, chart your course, fine-tune your internal GPS system, fill up your tank, and get rolling.

Your Super Aging lifestyle is waiting for you!

Essential Resources for Super Aging: Helping You Live a Life of Independence and Freedom

There is an abundance of government and private programs designed specifically for seniors and their unique needs. Some of them make life easier, some show you how to save money, and others help you look after your health and well-being.

The hardest part of accessing what these programs have to offer is finding them in the first place. In many cases, seniors have a problem or concern and have no idea something exists to help them. That's the purpose of the following list of resources—to discover and take advantage of everything available to you.

1. **Administration for Community Living** – Every American, regardless of age or disability status, has the inalienable right to live in their own home with the support they need in a community where they feel their contributions are valued. The U.S. Department of Health and Human Services (HHS) formed the Administration for Community Living (ACL) in 2012 to provide these things. The ACL joined the Administration on Aging (AoA), the Administration on Intellectual and Developmental Disabilities (AIDD), and the HHS Office on Disability to make one federal agency. That agency is charged with making community support more accessible, with special attention and resources for older Americans and those with disabilities. Visit https://acl.gov/.

2. **Administration on Aging** – The Administration on Aging (AoA) was created to oversee provisions in the Older Americans

Act of 1965. It provides programs and services that help older Americans be independent while living in their chosen communities and homes. The AoA gives the federal government power to allocate funds so states can offer services to support residents ages 61 and older. Visit https://acl.gov/about-acl/administration-aging.

3. **Alliance for Retired Americans** – The Community Advocacy Network (CAN) is a program established by the Alliance for Retired Americans and designed for individuals and communities so all seniors can have security in retirement and live a dignified life. It brings union and non-union members into the Alliance's advocacy programs, with a focus on expanding and protecting Medicare, Medicaid, Social Security, and pensions in an effort to multiply retirement security. Visit https://retiredamericans.org/.

4. **Alzheimer's Association** – A world free of Alzheimer's disease and all other dementias is the goal of the Alzheimer's Association, a voluntary organization focused on research, care, and support of Alzheimer's patients. Through the acceleration of international research, the reduction of risk, and early detection, the Alzheimer's Association is ensuring that high-risk individuals receive the best quality support and care. Visit https://www.alz.org/.

5. **Alzheimers.gov** – Alzheimer's disease is not part of the normal aging process, although it causes dementia in older adults more often than any other factor. It is a disorder of the brain that progresses slowly and negatively affects memory and cognition. Alzheimers.gov is a website dedicated to Alzheimer's education and advice for health professionals, caregivers, patients, and those at risk. Visit https://www.alzheimers.gov/.

6. **American Association for Geriatric Psychiatry** – The American Association of Geriatric Psychiatry (AAGP) specializes in geriatric psychiatry and represents and serves members

nationally. Through advocacy, clinical career development, education by professionals, and support for researchers and instructors, it promotes the well-being and good mental health of seniors. Visit https://www.aagponline.org/.

7. **American Association of Retired People** – Known as AARP, this organization makes recommendations on public policy for nearly 38 million seniors with diverse political views and lifestyles. AARP concentrates on the concerns of people over the age of 50, including finances, community, healthcare, affordable care, long-term care, consumer safeguards, and democracy for all. Visit https://www.aarp.org/.

8. **American Geriatrics Society** – Commonly called AGS, this organization works to improve older Americans' quality of life while promoting more independence and better health. AGS is a not-for-profit, nationwide organization made up of professionals in the field of geriatric healthcare, including more than 6,000 social workers, physician's assistants, internists, pharmacists, family practitioners, and geriatric doctors and nurses. It focuses on advocacy, particularly in the areas of patient care, public policy, research, and public education—all implemented through leadership provided to policymakers, healthcare professionals, and the public. Visit https://www.americangeriatrics.org/.

9. **American Seniors Association** – The conservative alternative to AARP, the American Seniors Association, offers benefit choices for a "healthier and wealthier life." The organization believes that seniors deserve more choices when deciding who will represent them in Washington, DC. As the nation's fastest-growing advocacy for older Americans, it works to secure the support, respect, and admiration that seniors deserve in exchange for the families they've built and the ways they've enhanced the quality of life in America. Visit https://americanseniors.org/.

10. **American Society on Aging** – Aging is a constantly changing field, and the American Society on Aging (ASA) has been guiding professionals through those changes for more than 65 years. It is the lone association serving authorities in a multidisciplinary manner. As times change, ASA has proved to be a priceless and unrivaled resource with a comprehensive perspective and an understanding of issues aging Americans face. Its mission is to expand and advance professionals' skills, help them leverage data and resources, and support their careers so they can better serve older Americans. Visit https://www.asaging.org/.

11. **Argentum** – As a leading nationwide organization, Argentum is singularly committed to supporting the professional operation and management of residential senior communities, as well as attending to older Americans and their families. It has been advocating for seniors' rights to independence, quality of life, dignity, and choice since 1990. Visit https://www.argentum.org/.

12. **Association of Mature American Citizens** – Known as AMAC, this organization provides trustworthy financial advice, healthcare guidance, and retirement and insurance support. It is rooted in American history, national traditions, the Constitution, the Bill of Rights, sustained morality, national solvency, and altruistic veterans. AMAC recognizes that we have inherited a rich legacy and want to repay the debt we owe. Visit https://amac.us/.

13. **Benefits.gov** – In 2002, GovBenefits.gov and was launched as one of the first eGovernment initiatives in the President's Management Agenda. Later changed to Benefits.gov, it is the federal government's official benefits website, supported, managed, and operated by a federal agency partnership. It gives citizens easy access to information about government benefits with simple eligibility and application guidance. Used by millions of

Americans, this comprehensive online resource serves senior citizens, caretakers, businesses, and state and federal entities. Visit https://www.benefits.gov/.

14. **Caregiver Action Network** – The Caregiver Action Network (CAN) is a leading national organization that serves family caregivers. It works to enhance the quality of the lives of 90 million US citizens who take care of family members suffering with complications from aging, chronic illness, and disabilities. Some examples of people CAN serves are parents with children who have substantial health difficulties, people who attend to wounded veterans, young couples dealing with chronic disease diagnoses, individuals who care for senior citizens, and grown children who are caring for parents with Alzheimer's disease. A nonprofit organization, CAN provides education, resources, and peer support to US family caregivers at no charge. Visit https://caregiveraction.org/.

15. **Catholic Golden Age** – Created in 1975 just for Catholics who are 50 and over, Catholic Golden Age is the largest organization of its kind. It provides current information about crucial issues for mature Catholics. This nonprofit organization was incorporated in the Commonwealth of Pennsylvania and has more than 1.25 million members. Visit https://catholicgoldenage.org/.

16. **Centers for Medicare & Medicaid Services** – This federal agency administers our nation's chief healthcare programs (Medicare, Medicaid, CHIP). Additionally, it collects data, analyzes it, conducts research, publishes reports, and works to eliminate fraud and program abuses. Visit https://www.cms.gov/.

17. **Corporation for National and Community Service** – This organization (made up of AmeriCorps, Senior Corps, Volunteer Generation Fund, and others) helps millions of US citizens better their own lives and the lives of others. By working with

local partners, it addresses America's most challenging issues by accessing the can-do spirit and ingenuity of Americans. Visit https://www.nationalservice.gov/.

18. **Eldercare Directory** – The people at Eldercare Directory are dedicated to helping seniors and those who care for them to discover the best providers and services for their unique needs. They also help visitors find answers to burning legal and financial questions and take advantage of all the government assistance programs available to older Americans. Those looking for help with in-home care, senior community living, full-time facility care, Medicare, Medicaid, governmental benefits, and more can find what they need at Eldercare Directory. Visit https://www.eldercaredirectory.org/.

19. **Eldercare Locator** – Since 1991, this national service has been connecting American seniors and their caregivers with state and local agencies, as well as trustworthy, community-based support and resources. Some examples of services that can be accessed are meals, in-home care, caregiver training, transportation, temporary care, and much more. Visit https://eldercare.acl.gov/.

20. **Fall Prevention Center of Excellence** – Based at the University of Southern California, Leonard Davis School of Gerontology, the Fall Prevention Center of Excellence (FPCE) promotes independent living and aging in place for people of all ages and abilities. Through research, training, and technical assistance, professionals can respond to a growing demand for home modifications and fall prevention in home environments. FPCE is also a home-modification information center for professionals as well as consumers, offering a wealth of information including the National Directory of Home Modification and Repair Resources. Visit https://homemods.org/.

21. **Family Caregiver Alliance** – The mission of the Family Caregiver Alliance (FCA) is to enhance the quality of life for family

caregivers and the family members they are caring for. More than 40 years ago, the FCA endeavored to provide services to caregivers serving adult family members with cognitive or physical impairments, including Parkinson's disease, Alzheimer's disease, stroke, and dementia. It helps assess and plan for care, enhance direct care skills, design wellness programs, offer respite services, and provide financial and legal vouchers for consultation. With their digital service platform, FCA offers ongoing support for caregivers on state, national, and international levels, focusing on health and social development, policy, research, and public awareness. Visit https://www.caregiver.org/.

22. **Five Wishes** – A human-centered, comprehensive, advance-care planning platform, Five Wishes gives healthcare providers what they need—a simple-to-use, proven method for having conversations that are not only compassionate but effective. Whether it's a sizable health system, hospice organization, clinic, physician, long-term care service, or other type of health practice, Five Wishes provides what is necessary to choose elements that are right for each situation. Most components can be customized according to specific needs, including who is being served and how advance care fits into particular practices. Visit https://fivewishes.org/.

23. **The Global Ageing Network** – The Global Ageing Network's mission is connection and support for elder service and care providers worldwide. It endeavors to improve the quality of life for those advancing in age. It promotes that mission with research, leadership, education, and collaboration. Businesses, governments, aging services, volunteer organizations, academics, architects, and researchers are among its members, all specializing in aging design. Visit https://globalageing.org/.

24. **Home Equity Conversion Mortgages** – As the FHA's reverse mortgage program, Home Equity Conversion Mortgages

(HECM) enables individuals to extract equity from their homes. Homeowners decide how to withdraw funds with choices, including fixed monthly payments, lines of credit, or both. Individuals may also use HECM to purchase a primary residence using on-hand cash to pay the difference between HECM earnings and the sale price. Visit https://www.benefits.gov/benefit/709.

25. **Honor Flight Network** – Honor Flight Network transports veterans of the United States military to visit war memorials in Washington, DC, at no cost to those veterans. This national network is made up of independent hubs working together to show our nation's honor and appreciation for the service of these brave men and women. Each veteran the Honor Flight Network flies to Washington, DC, has a unique opportunity to share the occasion with other veterans, to honor those who have made the ultimate sacrifice, to share stories, and to live this experience alongside others like them. Visit https://www.honorflight.org/about-us/.

26. **IRS Free-File Program** – Seniors can prepare and file their individual federal income tax returns at no cost through the IRS Free-File Program. The simple-to-use software does all the hard work. Visit https://www.irs.gov/filing/free-file-do-your-federal-taxes-for-free.

27. **Justice in Aging** – Formerly known as the National Senior Citizens Law Center, Justice in Aging is fighting senior poverty through law. This agency has been working since 1972 to help aging Americans—particularly those with limited resources, women, LGBTs, people of color, and those limited in the English language—to gain access to affordable healthcare and financial security. By focusing on helping those who have traditionally lacked legal attention, Justice in Aging provides resources, training, advocacy, and litigation to local agencies while ensuring personal access to social safety net programs,

including Social Security, Medicare, Medicaid, and Supplemental Security Income (SSI). Visit https://www.justiceinaging.org/.

28. **Leading Age** – The Leading Age service provides community-specific directories for locating not-for-profit services and housing. It is committed to delivering quality that is trustworthy and time-tested. Leading Age includes many organizations that have been serving older Americans for generations. Visit https://www.leadingage.org/.

29. **Meals on Wheels America** – There are more than 5,000 community Meals on Wheels programs across the United States. The organization is leading the fight against senior hunger and isolation. It supplies leadership, research, education, funding, support, advocacy, and empowerment to two million staff members and volunteers who deliver meals with high nutritional value and provide safety checks and friendly visits. Thanks to this service, seniors can retain their independence and dignity. Visit https://www.mealsonwheelsamerica.org/.

30. **Medicaid** – Millions of low-income adults, children, expectant mothers, seniors, disabled, and more can be eligible for Medicaid healthcare coverage. It is jointly funded, administered by individual states and monitored by the federal government. Visit https://www.medicaid.gov/.

31. **Medicare** – Medicare is health insurance provided by the federal government for Americans who are 65 and older, those of any age with disabilities, and those suffering with kidney failure that requires dialysis (end-stage renal disease, or ESRD). Medicare Part A is hospital insurance that covers inpatient stays, in-facility skilled nursing care, hospice, and some types of in-home care. Medicare Part B is medical insurance that covers outpatient care, some physicians' services, medical supplies, and preventive procedures. Medicare Part D is prescription drug coverage that supplements original Medicare, some

Medicare cost plans, some Medicare private fee-for-service plans, and Medicare Medical Savings Account plans. Insurance companies and other private companies that have been approved by Medicare offer these plans. Prescription drug coverage may also be offered if it follows the same guidelines as Medicare Prescription Drug programs. Visit https://www.medicare.gov/.

32. **Medicare Interactive** – An online health insurance reference center for older Americans and those with disabilities, Medicare Interactive (MI) is accessible only through the Medicare Rights Center and is offered at no cost. Americans with Medicare coverage have lots of questions, and MI strives to deliver easy-to-understand answers for caregivers and family members. MI has compiled and used attorneys' and counselors' best practices and expertise to design this service, which is presented in a number of formats and available 24/7. Visit https://www.medicareinteractive.org/.

33. **Medicare Rights Center** – This nonprofit, national service created for consumers is working to ensure access to affordable healthcare. Senior citizens and those with disabilities can find counseling, advocacy, education and public policy at the Medicare Rights Center. Visit https://www.medicarerights.org/.

34. **Health & Human Services Programs & Services** – The U.S. Department of Health & Human Services (HHS) oversees more than 100 programs in its divisions of operation. These programs deliver essential human services and look after all Americans' health, particularly those like seniors who may have difficulty helping themselves. Visit https://www.hhs.gov/programs.

35. **The National Academy of Elder Law Attorneys** – Known as NAELA, this is a professional association of attorneys dedicated to the improvement of legal services provided to aging Americans. Visit https://www.naela.org/.

36. **National Active and Retired Federal Employees** – The National Active and Retired Federal Employees (NARFE) is dedicated to the improvement of benefits for federal employees, both active and retired, as well as their spouses and survivors. It is a nonprofit, 501(c) association. With 300,000 members and more than 1,300 chapters, NARFE is present in nearly every state and in Washington, DC, Panama, Puerto Rico, and the Philippines. Electronic chapters are also available. NARFE members (or spouses and survivors) are covered by the Civil Service Retirement System (CSRS) or the Federal Employees Retirement System (FERS). Visit https://www.narfe.org/.

37. **National Aging and Disability Transportation Center** – Administered by the National Association of Area Agencies on Aging and Easterseals, this organization is part of the Federal Transit Administration (FTA). Guided by the Administration for Community Living (ACL), the National Aging and Disability Transportation Center promotes the accessibility and availability of transportation for those with disabilities, those of advanced age, and their caregivers. Visit https://www.nadtc.org/.

38. **Age in Place** – Age in Place was created by the National Aging in Place Council as a support network so aging consumers can continue to live healthy, active lives. Some chapters connect businesses and service providers to ensure that clients' needs are met. Visit https://www.ageinplace.org/.

39. **National Alliance for Caregiving** – The National Alliance for Caregiving (NAC) endeavors to improve the quality of life for those requiring care as well as their caregivers, family, and friends. Since 1996, this 501(c) nonprofit organization has advanced its mission through research, innovation, and advocacy. The NAC conducts research, performs policy analysis, generates national programs for best practices, and strives to enhance awareness of issues important to family caregivers. It

also offers technical assistance to caregiving coalitions across the country, with nearly 30 locales and states represented. The NAC is also the founder and secretariat for the International Alliance of Care Organizations (IACO). Most importantly, it actively recognizes family caregivers who provide crucial financial and social contributions while preserving the well-being of those they care for. Visit https://www.caregiving.org/.

40. **National Asian Pacific Center on Aging** – An American service and advocacy organization, the National Asian Pacific Center on Aging (NAPCA) serves senior Asian Americans and Pacific Islanders (AAPIs). It aims to assist the aging AAPI community with Social Security, Medicare, Medicaid, and other federal programs. It also offers a multilingual help line and strives to educate the public on the specific needs of this community. Visit https://www.napca.org/.

41. **National Association for Home Care & Hospice** – A non-profit entity, the National Association for Home Care & Hospice (NAHC) represents America's 33,000 hospice and home care organizations. Every year, 12 million Americans are chronically ill, disabled, or infirm. NAHC advocates for the more than two million aides, therapists, caregivers, and nurses who care for them. It is committed to excellence and works tirelessly to uphold the highest standards of care. Visit https://www.nahc.org/.

42. **National Association of Area Agencies on Aging** – The National Association of Area Agencies on Aging is a 501(c)(3) membership organization that represents the United States' 622 Area Agencies on Aging (AAAs). It gives a voice to the 250+ Title VI Native American programs in Washington, DC. It also helps federal lawmakers set priorities, build member capacity, make AAAs and Title VI programs more visible, train and educate, drive excellence in Information and Referral/Assistance (I&R/A), provide transportation, make communities livable,

and promote volunteerism—all in an effort to support its members' success. Visit https://www.n4a.org/.

43. **National Association of State Veterans Homes** – The National Association of State Veterans Homes (NASVH) promotes and enhances the life and quality of care for US military veterans and their families who are living in state veterans' homes. The organization's mission is carried out through networking, advocacy, and education. Visit https://www.nasvh.org/.

44. **National Care Planning Council** – The National Care Planning Council (NCPC) and its affiliates are committed to helping families understand the importance of planning and implementing long-term care for aging or disabled loved ones. The council's services are rooted in honesty, integrity, and an authentic concern for those who need or will need long-term care. Visit https://www.longtermcarelink.net/.

45. **National Caucus and Center on Black Aging** – The National Caucus and Center on Black Aging (NCBA) trains and places employees over the age of 50, improves quality of life, and advocates for health, well-being, and affordable housing without regard for ethnicity, race, or status. Visit https://ncba-aging.org/.

46. **National Resource Center on LGBT Aging** – As the United States' pioneer resource center for gay, lesbian, bisexual, and transgender seniors, the National Resource Center on LGBT Aging offers technical assistance, training, news, and more. Visit www.lgbtagingcenter.org.

47. **National Center on Elder Abuse** – The goal of the National Center on Elder Abuse (NCEA) is to improve our national response to elder abuse, exploitation, and neglect. The center gathers, disseminates, and stimulates innovative and validated methods for research, education, and policy. The NCEA's objectives are (1) to enhance the identification and reporting of elder abuse through the development and dissemination

of information to professionals; (2) to improve the ability of everyone in the senior network to identify, intervene, and prevent abuse with technical assistance, practical tools, collaboration, and innovative approaches; and (3) to stimulate and pioneer sustainable change in systems through the development of models, programs, and initiatives to decrease incidents of elder abuse. Visit https://ncea.acl.gov/.

48. **National Council on Aging** – With a vision to foster a caring and just society where every person can age with purpose, security, and dignity, the National Council on Aging (NCOA) has been working for more than 60 years to meet the challenges associated with aging. The council provides inventive programs and community services, advocacy, and online help alongside government agencies, businesses, and nonprofits. The NCOA's mission is to improve millions of older adults' lives, particularly those who struggle, and enhance the health and financial security of 40 million seniors by the year 2030. Visit https://www.ncoa.org/.

49. **National Council on Teacher Retirement** – An independent association, the National Council on Teacher Retirement (NCTR) is dedicated to preserving the integrity of public retirement systems in the United States and its territories. It also upholds the rights and benefits of present and future members. Founded in 1924, the NCTR affiliated itself with the National Education Association 13 years later. The association became independent in 1971 and is now a 501(c)(6) nonprofit entity with memberships in 63 local, territorial, and state systems. Visit https://nctr.org/.

50. **National Directory of Home Modification and Repair Resources** – This resource is a guide, sorted by state, to specialized architects, contractors, construction experts, remodelers, and interior designers who can renovate homes to fit the changing lifestyles and needs of older Americans and help

them maintain their independence. Visit https://homemods. org/national-directory/.

51. **National Hispanic Council on Aging** – The National Hispanic Council on aging (NHCOA) is leading the country in life improvements for older Hispanic adults and their family members and caregivers. For more than 30 years, the NHCOA has been a strong voice in Washington, DC (its headquarters), dedicating itself to education, promotion, advocacy, policy, and practice in the areas of financial security, health, and housing. Visit https://www.nhcoa.org/.

52. **National Hospice and Palliative Care Organization** – Representing patients in hospice and palliative care, the National Hospice and Palliative Care Organization works to increase access to a people-centered healthcare model. This leading organization strives to provide patients and their families with peace, dignity, and comfort through the most vulnerable periods of their lives. Visit https://www.nhpco.org/.

53. **National Indian Council on Aging**– Founded in 1976 by the National Tribal Chairmen's Association, the National Indian Council on Aging (NICOA) is a 501(c)(3) nonprofit. It started as a call to meet the needs of aging elders in the American Indian and Alaskan Native communities. The NICOA advocates for enhanced economics and comprehensive health and social services for these groups. Visit https://www.nicoa.org/.

54. **National Institute on Aging** – There are 27 institutes included in the National Institutes of Health (NIH), and the National Institute on Aging (NIA) is one of them. This organization uses science to understand aging and prolong healthy, active years. It is also the leading federal agency in research and support for Alzheimer's disease. Visit https://www.nia.nih.gov/.

55. **Parkinson's Foundation** – Making life better for those with Parkinson's disease is the mission of the Parkinson's Foundation. It strives to advance research, improve care, and move

toward a cure. The foundation is fueled by the passion, energy, and experience of the global Parkinson's community. Visit https://www.parkinson.org/.

56. **National Resource Center for Engaging Older Adults** – Funded by the National Association of Area Agencies on Aging (n4a), this national endeavor is supported by a number of diverse partner agencies and is funded by the U.S. Administration on Aging (part of the U.S. Administration for Community Living). The program, called engAGED, develops and promotes engagement opportunities for seniors with the help of a vast array of channels for the purpose of overcoming participation barriers. It specializes in the identification and empowerment of older adults for the valuable contributions and volunteerism they have to offer in their own communities. Visit https://www.n4a.org/engaged.

57. **The National Resource Center on Nutrition and Aging** – The National Resource Center on Nutrition and Aging (NRCNA) was created to offer nutrition and healthy-living assistance to the network of older adults in the United States. It works with regional, state, and national associations that are concerned with aging. It also implements the nutrition segments of the Older Americans Act. Visit https://nutritionandaging.org/national-resource-center-nutrition-aging.

58. **National Senior Games Association** – This biennial competition is specifically designed for those over the age of 50. It includes 19 sports and hosts the most significant multisport senior championship in the world. Visit https://nsga.com/.

59. **Nutrition Services Incentive Program** – Through the USDA's congregate and home-delivered nutrition programs, the Nutrition Services Incentive Program (NSIP) benefits seniors by funding states, US territories, and Indian tribal organizations to purchase food and cover costs for food commodities. Visit https://acl.gov/programs/health-wellness/nutrition-services.

60. **Pension Benefit Guaranty Corporation** – Founded by the Employee Retirement Income Security Act of 1974, the Pension Benefit Guaranty Corporation (PBGC) works to safeguard retirement income for more than three million private-sector workers. Employees who own defined benefit pension plans that provide monthly benefits after retirement count on PBGC to promote the continuation and maintenance of those pension plans, oversee uninterrupted and timely payments, and keep premiums to a minimum. Visit https://www.pbgc.gov/.

61. **Program of All-Inclusive Care for the Elderly** – PACE, or Program of All-Inclusive Care for the Elderly, offers comprehensive social and medical services to frail and community-dwelling aged Americans, especially those who are eligible for both Medicare and Medicaid. Visit https://www.medicare. gov/your-medicare-costs/get-help-paying-costs/pace.

62. **Senior Community Service Employment Program** – Founded in 1965, the Senior Community Service Employment Program (SCSEP) is our nation's longest-running program that helps low-income and unemployed people over the age of 55 find work. The program matches those who are eligible with part-time training operations for nonprofits. Visit https://www. ncoa.org/older-adults/money/work-retirement/scsep.

63. **AmeriCorps Seniors** – This network of nationwide service programs for 55-and-older Americans consists of three main programs, each with a unique approach to promote civic engagement and improve lives. AmeriCorps Seniors volunteers give their time and talents to fill critical needs in communities. Some examples include mentoring, academic tutoring, caring for the elderly, and disaster relief. Visit https://www.nationalservice.gov/programs/senior-corps.

64. **Senior Job Bank** – This meeting spot connects job seekers over the age of 50 with employers. Senior Job Bank took its services online in 1999 but had been in operation for 24 years prior to

that. Gene Burnard and the NHC Group, Inc. own and manage this resource with the goal of providing a service that covers all types of employment and disciplines. It serves part-time job seekers, those who are entering the workforce for the first time, skilled executives, and those continuing full-time careers. Visit http://www.seniorjobbank.org/.

65. **Center for Workforce Inclusion** – Previously known as Senior Service America, the Center for Workplace Inclusion helps low-income and otherwise disadvantaged mature adults participate fully in shaping their futures, as well as the futures of the communities they live in. Originally launched in 1962 as the National Council of Senior Citizens, it is currently the only nationwide entity exclusively dedicated to employing workers over the age of 50. It is a 501(c)(3) nonprofit organization head-quartered near Washington, DC, in Silver Spring, Maryland. Visit https://www.centerforworkforceinclusion.org/

66. **Service Corps of Retired Executives** – SCORE, or the Service Corps of Retired Executives, is the United States' largest network of expert business mentors who volunteer to help small businesses launch, grow, and achieve their goals. A 501(c)(3) nonprofit established in 1964, SCORE provides education and mentoring to more than 11 million entrepreneurs, partnered with the Small Business Administration (SBA). Through the selfless service of 10,000 volunteers and support from the SBA, most of SCORE's services are offered free of charge. Visit https://www.score.org/.

67. **Social Security Administration** – For more than 80 years, the Social Security Administration has been providing people with financial protection. Most Americans are either receiving Social Security benefits or know someone who is. This anti-poverty government program provides benefits to retirees, survivors, and the disabled. Social Security ensures both

today and tomorrow with financial support, exceptional customer service, and information security. Visit https://www.ssa.gov/.

68. **State Health Insurance Assistance Programs** – The State Health Insurance Assistance Programs (SHIP) provides in-depth and objective local insurance assistance and counseling to individuals who are eligible for Medicare, as well as their family members and caregivers. Visit https://www.shiptacenter.org/.

69. **State Pharmaceutical Assistance Programs** – The State Pharmaceutical Assistance Programs (SPAPs) are run by the states and offer prescription payment assistance to low-income seniors and disabled adults. Fewer than half of the states have an SPAP, but in the states where it's offered, Part D "wraparound" coverage (the program pays for what Medicare Part D does not) is generally provided. You can find out if your state has an SPAP by visiting https://www.medicare.gov/ and choosing your state from the dropdown menu. You may also visit https://www.medicare.gov/pharmaceutical-assistance-program/.

70. **USA.gov** – The mission of USA.gov is to generate and organize crucial government information and services in a timely fashion, making it accessible anytime, anywhere, and to anyone. Visit https://www.usa.gov/.

71. **U.S. Department of Veterans Affairs** – The Veterans Affairs (VA) is the United States' largest integrated healthcare network. It serves nine million veterans in 1,255 healthcare facilities. The VA guides service members as they transition out of military service and into civilian life, assisting with things such as education, life insurance, home loans, and more through the Veterans Benefits Administration. The National Cemetery Administration ensures that those who served this country aren't forgotten by providing dignified burial services in 142 cemeteries that are maintained as national shrines. They also

provide tributes that commemorate veterans' service and sacrifices. The VA enhances our nation's preparedness for terrorism, war, natural disasters, and national emergencies. It develops plans and takes action to ensure that veterans are continually served and supported, and that local, state, and national emergency management, safety, public health, and homeland security efforts are maintained. Visit https://www.va.gov/.

72. **U.S. Railroad Retirement Board** – The U.S. Railroad Retirement Board (RRB) is part of the executive branch of the federal government and acts as an independent agency. Its chief function is administering comprehensive unemployment, illness, retirement, and survivor benefits to America's retired railroad workers and their families under the Railroad Retirement and Railroad Unemployment Insurance Acts. The RRB also has administrative responsibilities as part of the Social Security Act, including Medicare coverage for railroad workers. In 2019, it disbursed retirement and survivor benefits totaling approximately $13 billion to 535,000 beneficiaries. Visit https://www.rrb.gov/.

73. **Women's Institute for a Secure Retirement** – A nonprofit organization, the Women's Institute for a Secure Retirement (WISER) helps policymakers, educators, and women understand important retirement income issues. No other establishment focuses solely on financial challenges that are specific to women. It uses partnerships, research, and programs to help women secure adequate income for retirement. A driver behind local and state events centered on long-term financial security, WISER works to level the playing field for women. Visit https://www.wiserwomen.org/.

Notes

Chapter One: The Super Aging Framework

1. "Life Expectancy of the World Population," Worldometers, accessed May 25, 2021, https://www.worldometers.info/demographics/life-expectancy.

2. "Satchel Paige," Wikipedia, accessed May 25, 2021, https://en.wikipedia.org/wiki/Satchel_Paige.

Chapter Two: The Super Aging Mindset: Moving from Fear to Empowerment

1   "What Does It Take to Be a Super-Ager?" Harvard Health Publishing, Harvard Medical School, May 1, 2017, https://www.health.harvard.edu/healthy-aging/what-does-it-take-to-be-a-super-ager.

2. Chris Hogan, *Retire Inspired* (Franklin, TN: Ramsey Press, 2016), xxii.

3. NPR, "Optimists for the Win: Finding the Bright Side Might Help You Live Longer," September 1, 2019, https://www.npr.org/sections/health-shots/2019/09/01/755185560/optimists-for-the-win-finding-the-bright-side-might-help-you-live-longer.

4. Matt Lloyd, "The Mind Game: How to Overcome Fear," Outside, December 10, 2014, https://www.climbing.com/skills/the-mind-game-how-to-overcome-fear.

Chapter Three: The Super Aging Health & Wellness Lifestyle: Achieving Better Health for a Better You

1. Tara Parker-Pope, "How to Build Healthy Habits," *The New York Times*, June 7, 2021, https://www.nytimes.com/2020/02/18/well/mind/how-to-build-healthy-habits.html.

2. Cleveland Clinic, "You Are Your Brain," accessed January 27, 2021, https://healthybrains.org/brain-facts.

3. "Nutrition and Healthy Eating," Mayo Clinic, accessed July 5, 2021, https://www.mayoclinic.org/healthy-lifestyle/nutrition-and-

healthy-eating/in-depth/water/art-20044256#:~:text=So%20
how%20much%20fluid%20does,fluids%20a%20day%20for%20
women

4. Betsy Mills, PhD, "Can Dehydration Impair Cognitive Function?"
January 10, 2020, https://www.alzdiscovery.org/cognitive-vitality/
blog/can-dehydration-impair-cognitive-function.

5. Expand-A-Lung, "Oxygen and Muscles," December 22, 2017,
https://expand-a-lung.com/oxygen-and-muscles.

6. Silver Sneakers, accessed January 27, 2021, https://tools.silvers-
neakers.com.

7. Sarah Olsen, "5 Incredible Athletes Who Accomplished Goals in
Old Age," Ayuda Care, August 15, 2018, https://medium.com/ayu-
da-care/5-incredible-athletes-who-accomplished-goals-in-old-
age-ea29b3838883.

8. Keith Pearson, "The MIND Diet: A Detailed Guide for Beginners,"
Healthline, accessed January 27, 2021, https://www.healthline.
com/nutrition/mind-diet.

9. Kumar Ravi, "16 Super Herbs and Spices That Lower Blood Sugar
Amazingly," Medium, September 28, 2019, https://medium.com/@
kumarravi_96309/16-super-herbs-and-spices-to-lower-blood-
sugar-amazingly-702e6a131c7e.

10. "Nir Barzilai, MD, Scientific Director," American Federation for
Aging Research, accessed January 27, 2021, https://www.afar.org/
nir-barzilai.

**Chapter Four: Super Aging Relationships: Staying Connected
during Retirement**

1. Nanci Hellmich, "Hundreds of Retirees Share Secrets to a
Happy Marriage," *USA Today*, January 6, 2015, https://www.
usatoday.com/story/money/personalfinance/2015/01/06/
retirees-love-marriage/20648553.

2. Karin Evans, "Why Relationships Are the Secret to Healthy
Aging," *Greater Good Magazine*, September 14, 2018, https://

greatergood.berkeley.edu/article/item/why_relationships_
are_the_secret_to_healthy_aging.

3. David Smith, "Why and How Do Friendships Change as We Age?"
The Power of Silence, accessed July 1, 2021, https://thepowerofsi-
lence.co/why-and-how-do-friendships-change-as-we-age.

4. Kira M. Newman, "Friends Help Our Health as We Age," *Greater
Good Magazine*, February 2, 2016, https://greatergood.berkeley.
edu/article/item/friends_help_our_health_as_we_age.

5. H. Tankovska, "Online Dating in the United States – Statistics & Facts," Statista, May 26, 2021, https://www.statista.com/
topics/2158/online-dating.

6. Mary Kane, "Finding Romance Later in Life," Kiplinger, March 12,
2018, https://www.kiplinger.com/article/retirement/t048-c000-
s004-senior-dating-advice-finding-romance-later-in-life.html.

7. Kevin Burger, "Aging Families: Older Adult Children
and Their Parents," *Health & Wellness*, January 17, 2019,
https://bethesdahealth.org/blog/2019/01/17/the-new-
aging-family-older-adults-and-parents.

8. Kathryn Slattery, "4 Tips from a Mother Caregiving for
Her Mother," Guideposts, accessed July 1, 2021, https://
www.guideposts.org/caregiving/family-caregiving/
aging-parents/4-tips-from-a-mother-caregiving-for-her-mother.

9. Pew Research Center, "Social Media Fact Sheet," April 7, 2021,
https://www.pewresearch.org/internet/fact-sheet/social-media.

Chapter Five: Super Aging Retirement Readiness: Preparing Your Finances for Retirement

1. Paul Brandus, "Opinion: Why Your First Five Years of Retirement Are Critical," Market Watch, July 4, 2020, https://
www.marketwatch.com/story/why-your-first-five-years-of-
retirement-are-critical-2020-06-22.

2. U.S. Bureau of Labor Statistics, "Consumer Expenditures–2019,"
September 9, 2020, https://www.bls.gov/news.release/cesan.nr0.
htm.

3. "The Life Expectancy Calculator," Living to 100, accessed July 5, 2021, https://www.livingto100.com.

4. Leandro Mueller, "How to Choose the Right Supplemental Insurance for Medicare," Free MedSupp Quotes, September 13, 2017, https://freemedsuppquotes.com/choose-best-supplemental-insurance-for-medicare.

5. Stella Severino, "5 Retirement Stories That Will Inspire You," SafeNews, April 18, 2020, https://safe365.com/blog/en/5-retirement-stories-that-will-inspire-you.

6. Merrill Lynch, "New Retirement Survey," Age Wave, accessed July 2021, https://agewave.com/what-we-do/landmark-research-and-consulting/research-studies/new-retirement-survey.

7. Tom Alberts, "Original Owner of Bush Family Home Made a Texas-Sized Estate Planning Mistake," Legacy Assurance Plan, November 21, 2019, https://legacyassuranceplan.com/articles/estate-stories/Bush-family-home-estate-plan-mistake.

Chapter Six: Super Aging Purpose of Life: Discovering Your Destiny

1. Ana Cocarla, "Finding Meaning and Purpose in Old Age," SeniorCare Center, accessed July 1, 2021, https://srcarecenter.com/article/finding-meaning-and-purpose-in-old-age.

2. Federal Interagency Forum on Aging Related Statistics, *Older Americans: Key Indicators of Well-Being*, 2020, https://www.aging-stats.gov/docs/LatestReport/OA20_508_10142020.pdf.

3. "30 Stories about the Touching Kindness of Strangers That'll Make You Tear Up," *Reader's Digest*, March 15, 2021, https://www.rd.com/article/kindness-strangers.

4. Dayna Winter, "Starting a Retirement Business: How This Former Teacher Became an Alpaca Rancher," Shopify Blog, May 20, 2020, https://www.shopify.com/blog/retirement-business.

5. "61 Jim Rohn Quotes on Success, Habits, and Achieving Your Goals," Develop Good Habits, accessed July 1, 2021, https://www.developgoodhabits.com/jim-rohn-quotes.

6. Jackie Green and Lauren Green McAfee, "How the Story of Your Life Changes the World for Generations to Come," Ann Voskamp (blog), accessed July 1, 2021, https://annvoskamp.com/2018/05/how-the-story-of-your-life-changes-the-world-for-generations-to-come.

Chapter Seven: Super Aging Emotional Mastery: Avoiding the 7 Deadly Sins of Aging

1. Marc Brackett, Ph.D. and Christina Cipriano, Ph.D., "Emotional Intelligence Comes of Age," Cerebrum Dana Foundation, July 15, 2020, https://dana.org/article/emotional-intelligence-comes-of-age.

2. Mayo Clinic Staff, "How to Live Your Best Life in Retirement," Mayo Clinic, May 23, 2019, https://www.mayoclinic.org/healthy-lifestyle/healthy-aging/in-depth/how-to-live-your-best-life-in-retirement/art-20390076.

3. Life & Learn, the Foundation for European Initiatives, "Emotional Intelligence and the Elderly: An Introduction for Teachers," October 2015, https://www.ids.pt/pdfs/module_2.pdf.

4. Stacey Burling, "Joy in the Age of Loss," *The Inquirer*, September 14, 2018, https://www.inquirer.com/health/inq/you-have-go-losses-pile-up-seniors-find-ways-stay-happy-20180914.html.

5. Karen Lawson, MD, "How Do Thoughts and Emotions Affect Health?" University of Minnesota, accessed July 1, 2021, https://www.takingcharge.csh.umn.edu/how-do-thoughts-and-emotions-affect-health.

6. Institute on Aging, "Stress Management for Seniors: Strategies for Empowering Your Aging Loved One," June 14, 2018, https://blog.ioaging.org/activities-wellness/stress-management-for-seniors-strategies-for-empowering-your-aging-loved-one.

7. Anxiety & Depression Association of America, "What Is Anxiety and Depression?" accessed July 1, 2020, https://adaa.org/understanding-anxiety.

8. Samantha Gluck, "Depression Quotes & Sayings That Capture Life with Depression," Healthy Place, April 21, 2020,

https://www.healthyplace.com/insight/quotes/depression-quotes-and-sayings-about-depression.

9. Closer Staff, "Barbra Streisand Shares How She Overcame Stage Fright: 'I Did a Lot of Work on Myself,'" Closer, March 28, 2018, https://www.closerweekly.com/posts/barbra-streisand-overcame-stage-fright-156916.

10. Sarah Fielding, "New Study Shows 91 Percent of Fears Don't Come True," BestLife, August 8, 2019, https://bestlifeonline.com/anxiety-vs-reality-study.

Chapter Eight: Super Aging Home & Community: Discovering the Best Place to Super Age

1. "Dan Buettner Quotes," Brainy Quote, accessed July 1, 2021, https://www.brainyquote.com/authors/dan-buettner-quotes.

2. Dan Buettner, "Power 9®: Reverse Engineering Longevity," Blue Zones, accessed July 1, 2021, https://www.bluezones.com/2016/11/power-9.

3. Corinne Purtill, "Stop Me If You've Heard This One: A Robot and a Team of Irish Scientists Walk into a Senior Living Home," *Time*, October 4, 2019, https://time.com/longform/senior-care-robot.

4. Benjamin Harris, "Making Aging in Place Easier with Predictive Analytics," Healthcare IT News, March 29, 2019, https://www.healthcare-itnews.com/news/making-aging-place-easier-predictive-analytics.

5. "Safe at Home," Rebuilding Together, accessed July 1, 2021, https://rebuildingtogether.org/safe-at-home.

6. Linda Abbit, "Tiny Houses: The Next Big Thing for Seniors?" Senior Planet, accessed July 1, 2021, https://seniorplanet.org/tiny-houses-the-next-big-thing-for-seniors.

7. Kathleen Coxwell, "The Best Places to Retire: 24 Lists and Quizzes Plus Tips for Making the Best Relocation Decision for You," New Retirement, October 26, 2020, https://www.newretirement.com/retirement/best-places-to-retire/?amp=1.

8. Cynthia G. Simison, "Columnist Barbara Bernard Celebrates 90 Wonderful Years: Viewpoint," *Mass Live*, January 7, 2019, https://www.masslive.com/living/2017/07/columnist_barbara_bernard_celebrates_90_viewpoint.html.

9. Jeffrey Shaw, "Life Can Turn on a Dime," *HuffPost*, February 12, 2015, https://www.huffpost.com/entry/life-can-turn-on-a-dime_b_6674200.

10. "Aging and Disability Resource Centers," Administration for Community Living, December 13, 2017, https://acl.gov/programs/aging-and-disability-networks/aging-and-disability-resource-centers.

11. Genworth, "Cost of Care Survey," February 12, 2021, https://www.genworth.com/aging-and-you/finances/cost-of-care.html.

12. Centers for Disease Control and Prevention, "Alzheimer's Disease and Healthy Aging," October 26, 2020, https://www.cdc.gov/aging/aginginfo/alzheimers.htm.

13. "Best Nursing Homes Ratings," *U.S. News & World Report*, accessed July 1, 2021, https://health.usnews.com/best-nursing-homes.

14. The Villages, accessed July 1, 2021, https://www.thevillages.com.

Chapter Nine: Super Aging Perks: Amazing Things No One Told You about Aging

1. Tricia Cusden, "Enjoying a Third, Fabulous Act in Life," Live Long Master Aging, podcast, accessed July 2, 2021, http://www.llamapodcast.com/tricia-cusden.

2. Julie Deardorff, "Trust Increases with Age, Benefits Well Being: New Research Suggests a Bright Side to Getting Older," Northwestern Now, March 18, 2015, https://news.northwestern.edu/stories/2015/03/trust-increases-with-age-and-well-being.

3. "Regain Your Confidence," Harvard Health Publishing, Harvard Medical School, June 1, 2019, https://www.health.harvard.edu/staying-healthy/regain-your-confidence.

4. Nicole Didyk, MD, "How Sex Changes with Aging (& What You Can Do about It)," Better Health While Aging, accessed July 2, 2021, https://betterhealthwhileaging.net/how-sex-changes-in-aging-and-what-to-do.

5. Jeewon Oh, "Do We Become More Empathetic as We Get Older?" Society for Personality and Social Psychology, June 12, 2020, empathetic study https://www.spsp.org/news-center/blog/oh-empathy-over-time.

6. Donna Pols Trump, "Does Getting Older Make You Less Stressed?" Next Avenue, June 13, 2019, https://www.nextavenue.org/getting-older-less-stressed.

7. Adam Gorlick, "Stanford Study Shows Getting Older Leads to Emotional Stability, Happiness," Stanford Report, October 27, 2010, https://news.stanford.edu/news/2010/october/older-happy-study-102710.html.

8. BibleGateway, Ecclesiastes 3:11, NLT, https://www.biblegateway.com/passage/?search=Ecclesiastes+3%3A11&version=NLT.

Chapter Ten: Super Aging in America: How Super Agers Respond to Growing Trends

1. United States Census Bureau, "65 and Older Population Grows Rapidly as Baby Boomers Age," June 25, 2020, https://www.census.gov/newsroom/press-releases/2020/65-older-population-grows.html.

2. Board of Governors of the Federal Reserve System, "Report on the Economic Well-Being of U.S. Households in 2018," May 2019, Revised January 30, 2020, https://www.federalreserve.gov/publications/files/2018-report-economic-well-being-us-households-201905.pdf.

3. U.S. Department of Labor, Bureau of Labor Statistics, "Employment Projections — 2019–2029," September 1, 2020, https://www.bls.gov/news.release/pdf/ecopro.pdf.

4. Harriet Edleson, "More Americans Working Past 65," AARP, April 22, 2019, https://www.aarp.org/work/employers/info-2019/americans-working-past-65.html.

5. Tom Miles, "China Overtakes U.S. for Healthy Lifespan: WHO data," May 30, 2018, https://www.reuters.com/article/us-health-lifespan/china-overtakes-u-s-for-healthy-lifespan-who-data-idUSKCN1IV15L.

6. National Institute on Aging, "Geroscience: The Intersection of Basic Aging Biology, Chronic Disease, and Health," accessed July 2, 2021, https://www.nia.nih.gov/research/dab/geroscience-intersection-basic-aging-biology-chronic-disease-and-health.

7. National Conference of State Legislatures and AARP, "Aging in Place: A State Survey of Livability Policies and Practices," December 2011, https://assets.aarp.org/rgcenter/ppi/liv-com/ib190.pdf.

8. Genworth, "Genworth 17th Annual Cost of Care Survey: COVID-19 Exacerbates Already Rising Long Term Care Costs; Care Providers Foresee Additional Rate Hikes in 2021," accessed July 2, 2021, https://newsroom.genworth.com/2020-12-02-Genworth-17th-Annual-Cost-of-Care-Survey-COVID-19-Exacerbates-Already-Rising-Long-Term-Care-Costs-Care-Providers-Foresee-Additional-Rate-Hikes-in-2021.

9. Robotics Online Marketing Team, "The Future of Elder Care Is Service Robots," Association for Advancing Automation, May 13, 2020, https://www.robotics.org/blog-article.cfm/The-Future-of-Elder-Care-is-Service-Robots/262.

10. U.S. Department of Health and Human Services, Administration for Community Living, "2019 Profile of Older Americans," May 2020, https://acl.gov/sites/default/files/Aging%20and%20Disability%20in%20America/2019ProfileOlderAmericans508.pdf.

11. "Welcome to the AARP Network of Age-Friendly States and Communities," AARP, accessed July 2, 2021, https://www.aarp.org/livable-communities/network-age-friendly-communities.

12. Joe Kita, "Workplace Age Discrimination Still Flourishes in America," AARP, December 30, 2019, https://www.aarp.org/work/

working-at-50-plus/info-2019/age-discrimination-in-america.html.

13. Richard Eisenberg, "A New Ageism? The Fallout from the Pandemic," Forbes, July 21, 2020, https://www.forbes.com/sites/nextavenue/2020/07/21/a-new-ageism-the-fallout-from-the-pandemic/?sh=2350c5c86beb.

14. San Francisco Human Services Agency, "San Francisco Launches Innovative Ageism Awareness Campaign to Help Create a More Inclusive City," October 16, 2019, https://www.sfhsa.org/about/announcements/san-francisco-launches-innovative-ageism-awareness-campaign-help-create-more.

Chapter Eleven: Super Aging Champion: Taking the Next Step

1. AARP, "Disrupt Aging: The National Bestseller Now in Paperback (Updated Edition)," April 10, 2018, https://www.aarp.org/disrupt-aging/info-2016/joann-jenkins-disrupt-aging-book.html.

Acknowledgments

I would like to give a heartfelt thanks to my family and friends who contributed to Super Aging. First and foremost, thanks to my amazing wife, Hina, for her constant love, encouragement, and support. Without her, this book would not have been completed. And thank you to our terrific children, Graham, Ria, Connor and Rikhil, who inspire me each and every day.

A special thanks to my wonderful friends Jack Bevan, Deloris Wright, Jon and Beverly Thompson, Michelle McCarthy, Steve Greenstein and Christy Skinner for helping make Super Aging even better. To the exceptional team at The Legacy Foundation . . . thank you for making my life richer in countless ways.

Thanks to my talented literary and design team of Jennifer Waddle, Sue Vander Hook, Teresa Hawksworth and Sue Balcer who helped make Super Aging look and feel professional.

And a warm thank you to the Shell Point family, including my co-workers and colleagues, and most of all, the amazing "super aging" residents who have brought such joy and happiness to my life over the past three decades.

Made in the USA
Monee, IL
06 June 2022

97570937R00103